APPLYING SKILLS FOR HIGHER GCSE 4–9 MATHS EXAMS

Michael White

Elmwood Education

First published 2016 by
Elmwood Education Limited
Unit 5 Mallow Park
Watchmead
Welwyn Garden City
Herts. AL7 1GX
Tel. 01707 333232

ISBN 9781 906 622 633

Typeset and illustrated by Tech-Set Ltd., Gateshead, Tyne and Wear.

PREFACE

This stand-alone book provides banks of questions which have been written to complement any GCSE resources.

The questions focus on assessment objectives AO2 and AO3, ie. reasoning, interpreting, communicating and solving non-routine problems.

There are 28 sets of questions which can be used throughout the GCSE course or as more of a revisional aid. They may be tackled initially by groups of students to explore and discuss strategies or worked at individually. The majority of the sets of questions involve a mixture of topics which is essential if the students are to recall and select appropriate techniques. Some exercises are specific to Number, Algebra, Geometry or Statistics only. Ratio and proportion run throughout these.

Users of the main Elmwood Education Higher GCSE Maths 4–9 textbook will find links to this book in the answer section. The topics for each question are referenced in an index at the back of the book to assist if a particular topic needs to be chosen.

Students find the kind of questions in this book very demanding. The author has tried to provide a reasonable spread of complexity within each unit. Many schools have used units in Part One on a fortnightly basis in Year 10 then units in Part Two on a fortnightly basis in Year 11.

Michael White

iv

CONTENTS LIST

PART ONE

NUMBER 1

1 Mr Kenwood is working out the cost of his next gas bill.

> ### Gas Meter Readings
> Previous reading: 31789
> Present reading: 33004

He has to pay:

16.8p for the first 400 units used

11.2p for the remaining units used

He also pays a standing charge of £18.50

The total bill for the above is then subject to VAT at 5%.

How much will Mr. Kenwood have to pay for this gas bill?

> **Hint:**
> Firstly subtract the previous reading from the present reading to find out how many units of gas have been used.

2 Tom works out that

$$4\tfrac{2}{5} + 3\tfrac{1}{3} = 7\tfrac{3}{8}$$

Explain clearly the mistake that Tom has made.
Without using a calculator, work out the correct answer, showing all steps clearly.

3 Logan, Anjali, Naomi and Gavin want to see a film at the cinema.
A ticket at the Cresswall Cinema is £7.60

A ticket at the Albert Cinema is £6.50

The friends can each get to the Cresswall Cinema by bus for £7.90 return. There is no bus to the Albert Cinema.

They can get a taxi to either cinema.

> Cost of taxi   £1.30 per mile

Which cinema and type of transport will be the cheapest option for the 4 friends if the Cresswall Cinema is 12 miles away and the Albert Cinema is 14 miles away?

Explain your reasons.

4   Without using a calculator, write the following surds in order of size, starting with the smallest.

$4\sqrt{3}$ $\sqrt{47}$ 7

$3\sqrt{5}$ $5\sqrt{2}$ $\sqrt{46}$

Hint:
Firstly write each number in the form $\sqrt{n}$ before the surd was simplified.

5   Sophie's three children eat cereal every morning for their breakfast.

The fraction of a box of cereal eaten each morning by each child is shown below.

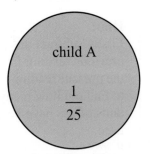
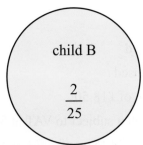
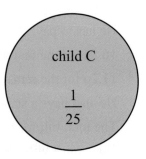

child A $\dfrac{1}{25}$

child B $\dfrac{2}{25}$

child C $\dfrac{1}{25}$

What is the least number of boxes of cereal that Sophie will need to buy to last the entire month of June?
Explain your working out fully.

6

The bars above show the amount of fuel in Avery's car.

Each bar shows $\frac{1}{8}$ of the petrol in the car's tank.

A gallon of petrol costs £7.56

Avery fills up this petrol tank completely which costs a further £42.

Assuming that one gallon is 4.5 litres, how many litres does Avery's petrol tank contain when it is full?

7   Rio says that $\sqrt{a} + \sqrt{b} = \sqrt{a + b}$ always.
    Katrina does not agree.
    Explain who is correct, giving clear reasons for
    your answer.

> **Hint:**
> Try some actual values for a and b.

8   $\dfrac{\sqrt{75}}{2\sqrt{n}} = \dfrac{5}{2}$ Find the value of n, showing clearly each step of your working out.

9   Ten friends plan a day trip to the seaside.

    They can get there by minibus taxi or by train.

    The prices are shown below:

> Train │ £15.60 day return

> Minibus taxi for 10 people £103.50

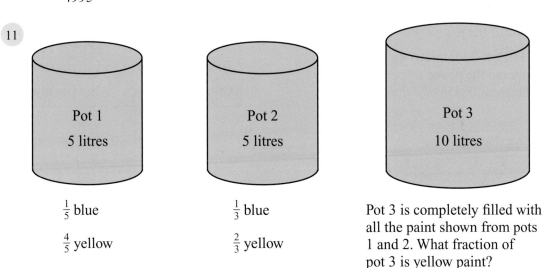

Each friend has a train railcard which
gives each one of them a 30% discount.

(a) The minibus appears to be cheaper. How much will each friend save
    compared to using the train?

(b) On the day, one friend is ill. The other 9 friends still have to use the taxi.
    This is now more expensive for each of them than using the train. By how much?

10 Without using a calculator, explain fully why

$$\frac{409}{4995} > 0.0\dot{8}1\dot{7}$$

11

Pot 1

5 litres

$\frac{1}{5}$ blue

$\frac{4}{5}$ yellow

Pot 2

5 litres

$\frac{1}{3}$ blue

$\frac{2}{3}$ yellow

Pot 3

10 litres

Pot 3 is completely filled with
all the paint shown from pots
1 and 2. What fraction of
pot 3 is yellow paint?

4

12

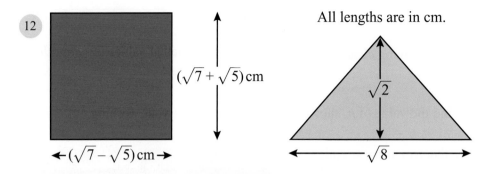

$(\sqrt{7} + \sqrt{5})\,$cm

$\leftarrow (\sqrt{7} - \sqrt{5})\,$cm $\rightarrow$

All lengths are in cm.

$\sqrt{2}$

$\leftarrow \sqrt{8} \rightarrow$

Which area is greater – the rectangle or the triangle? Do not use a calculator and show all your working out.

13

$$\frac{2}{5} = \frac{4}{10} = 0.4$$

$$8 = \frac{8}{1}$$

$$0.\dot{1}\dot{7} = \frac{17}{99}$$

Darryl says that any number can be written as a fraction. Is he correct? Justify your answer fully.

14 Ella's phone call summary on her last phone bill is shown below.

Type of call	No of calls	Total duration
To a UK phone line	205	12:25:24
To a UK mobile	128	4:49:45
To an 0845/0870 number	10	23:30
Other calls	5	35:06
Total	348	18:13:45

Some of the phone rates are shown opposite.

If Ella's bill for all her calls was £77.43, work out the phone rate per minute for calls to an 0845/0870 number.

To a UK phone line	5p per minute
To a UK mobile	12p per minute
Other calls	10p per minute

15 Prove that

$$\frac{3 + \sqrt{2}}{\sqrt{2}} + \frac{6 + \sqrt{8}}{\sqrt{8}} = 3\sqrt{2} + 2$$

You must show every step of your working out.

N | NUMBER 2

1   Natalie has £4500 to invest for 3 years. Two possible accounts are shown below.

SURE ACCOUNT	STEP ACCOUNT
3% per annum compound interest	2% for Year 1 3% for Year 2 4% for Year 3 The percentage is calculated on the amount of money in the account at the end of the year

Hint:
For compound interest, work out the interest for each year separately then add on to the total money. Maybe use a multiplier?

Which account will give Natalie more money at the end of 3 years and by how much?

2   Mark says that 'for any positive number n, n^2 is greater than n'.
Is this true or false? Give clear reasons for your answer.

3   Alexa and 3 friends need to book their summer holiday.
They plan to share two twin rooms at the Regala hotel.
The cost of the rooms is shown below.

	6th June– 3rd July		4th July– 7th August		8th August– 12th September		13th September– 15th October	
	7 nights	14 nights	7 nights	14 nights	7 nights	14 nights	7 nights	14 nights
Single room	£525	£675	£595	£765	£625	£780	£575	£720
Double room	£605	£775	£675	£865	£705	£880	£645	£800
Twin room	£605	£785	£685	£880	£715	£895	£645	£810
SPECIAL OFFER: 2% discount for every month in advance that full payment is made up to a maximum of six months.								

Each price shown above is the price per person.

Alexa and her friends wish to go on 15th August for 14 nights.

Alexa has £245. She borrows the remaining cost of the holiday from her parents.

She pays for the holiday on 28th March.
She repays her parents all the money over five months in equal monthly amounts.
How much is each monthly amount?

4 The price of a jacket is reduced by 20% in a sale. The jacket now costs £48.

Kayla wants to find out the original price of the jacket so she does the following calculation:

20% of 48 = 0.2 × 48 = 9.60
original cost = 48 + 9.60 = £57.60

(a) Explain clearly what mistake Kayla has made.

(b) Work out the original cost of the jacket.

5  Donald buys 60 golf balls in Britain for £81.
He takes them on a golfing holiday in the USA.
He gradually loses all the golf balls and decides to buy another 60.

He finds the same make of golf ball sold in boxes of twelve for $25.41

Using the exchange rate shown below, were the new golf balls cheaper or more expensive than the old ones and by how much?

£1 = $1.54

Hint:
Beware the amounts of golf balls.

6 A recipe for making 8 chocolate cookies is shown below.

120 g butter

120 g sugar

1 egg

200 g plain flour

30 g cocoa powder

100 g chocolate chips

Hayden has six 225 g packs of butter, two 500 g bags of sugar, one 1 kg bag of sugar, three boxes of 12 eggs, three 1kg bags of plain flour, two 225 g tins of cocoa powder and four 400 g bags of chocolate chips.

Hayden wants to make as many chocolate cookies as possible but can only make them in batches of eight.

Work out the greatest number of chocolate cookies that Hayden can make with his ingredients.

7　Prove that $2^0 = 1$

> **Hint:**
> Remember that $2^n \div 2^n = 2^{n-n}$

8　The costs of sending letters and packets are shown below.

Letter	1st class	2nd class
up to 100 g	43p	29p

Large letter	1st class	2nd class
up to 100 g	60p	46p
up to 250 g	85p	60p
up to 500 g	£1.15	75p

Packet	1st class	2nd class
up to 100 g	£1.24	£1.01
up to 250 g	£1.57	£1.35
up to 500 g	£2.04	£1.72
up to 750 g	£2.64	£2.20
up to 1 kg	£3.25	£3.85
up to 1.5 kg	£5.18	£4.49
up to 2 kg	£6.62	£5.79

Sarah sends four packets by 2nd class post weighing 184 g, 275 g, 1100 g and 1.85 kg. She also sends five large letters by 2nd class post each weighing 150 g and two large letters by 1st class post each weighing 420 g.

Finally she sends a number of letters by 1st class post.

If the total cost is £23.81, how many letters did she send?

9　Aryan, Ruhi and Maya are given some money.
The ratio of Aryan's share to Ruhi's share is 3:8.
The ratio of Ruhi's share to Maya's share is 1:3.
What is the ratio of Aryan's share to Maya's share?

10　Denton brings some bottles of wine back from France in his van. He gives 80% of the wine to a friend.

His brother, sister and father receive the remaining wine in the ratio 2:1:5.

Denton bought all the wine in boxes of twelve. If he gave his father 45 bottles of wine, how many boxes did Denton bring back from France?

11　Ron earns 40% of Sophie's salary.
Ron earns 75% of Sam's salary.
What percentage of Sophie's salary does Sam earn?
Show all your working out clearly.

12 Rob uses his credit card whilst visiting Holland.
    The conditions regarding the use of the credit card
    are shown below.

| Credit card |
| Exchange rate: £1 = €1.08 |
| Commission fee: 1.5% of any transaction |

Rob makes four transactions of €68.04, €28.08, €25.92 and €52.92.

How much commission (in £) does Rob have to pay in total?

13 Lin works out $27^{-\frac{1}{3}} \times 32^{\frac{4}{5}} \times 4^{-\frac{1}{2}}$ without using a calculator.
    She gets the answer 96.

    (a) Describe what mistakes she might have made.

    (b) What is the correct answer?

14 In 2010 there are 15 000 modern factories in the UK.

    In 2011 this total increases by $\frac{3}{20}$ of this amount.

    The ratio of old factories to modern factories is then 2:3

    In 2012, half the old factories are knocked down
    and rebuilt as modern factories.

    What is the new ratio of old factories to
    modern factories?

15

Some cyclists go out to train on each Saturday.

On Saturday, March 7th, they travel just 15 km.

On each subsequent Saturday they increase the distance
by 10% of the distance travelled on the previous Saturday.

On what date will they first travel more than 45 km?

M | MIXED 1

1 Mr Simpson has his house insured for £288 000.

He also has contents insurance to cover items in his house in case they are stolen or damaged.

The maximum amount the insurance firm will pay out for contents is 15% of Mr Simpson's house insurance.

Unfortunately Mr Simpson's house is burgled. The stolen items and their values are shown below.

Item	Value	% of brand new cost
Jewellery	£4776	100%
TV1	£468	60%
Computer	£1190	85%
TV2	£328	40%

The insurance firm pays out the brand new cost for each item.

What percentage of the maximum contents cover is paid out by the insurance firm on this occasion?

Hint: Think 'reverse percentages'.

2

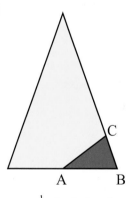
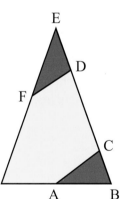
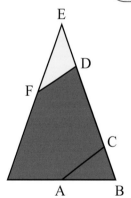

$\frac{1}{8}$ shaded red $\frac{2}{7}$ shaded red

What fraction of the triangle is shaded red in the last diagram?

3 The table opposite shows the exchange rates between the UK and Mexico as well as the UK and the USA.

Katerina buys a jumper for $61.56 in the USA.
Mira buys the same jumper for 828.75 pesos in Mexico.

£1 = 21.25 pesos
£1 = $1.62

In which country was the jumper cheaper? Show your full working out.

4

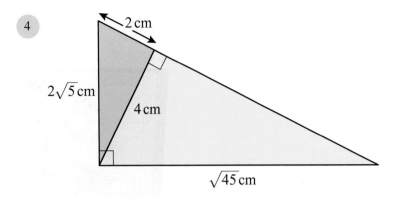

What percentage of the large triangle above is shaded blue?

Hint:
A as a percentage of B
is $\dfrac{A}{B} \times 100\%$

5   Dylan and five friends want to watch either motorcycle racing or go-karting.

The motorcycle racing costs £15.50 per person and is six miles from Dylan's house.

The go-karting costs £12.50 per person and is nine miles from Dylan's house.

The local taxi firm charges the following:

| Cab for four people £2.70 per mile |
| Cab for nine people £5.50 per mile |

Dylan and his friends wish to go by taxi. They choose the event which will cost them the least money for entry to the event and a taxi there and back to Dylan's house.

How much cheaper per person is this choice?

6   Company A increases its profit by 5% one year then by a further 5% the following year.

Company B increases its profit by 10% over the same two year period.

Is the profit increase the same for Company A and Company B during these two years?

Explain your answer fully.

7   $\boxed{?} \div \boxed{?} = 24a^3b^2$

Write down 3 pairs of terms which divide to give the answer $24a^3b^2$.

Hint:
$a^m \div a^n = a^{m-n}$

8 Scientists are trying to calculate the
likely number of frogs in a certain region.
They estimate the number of frogs now.

They work out that if each year the frog
population reduces by 10% of the
population at the start of the year,
there will be 17496 frogs after 3 years.

If the percentage reduction is only
5% each year, what would the expected
frog population be after 3 years?

9 Colin invests £1000 in a bank during the year 2012.

His money gains 4% per annum compound interest.

After three years the interest rate is reduced to 3%.

Colin finally withdraws his money when it reaches £1500.

During which year does Colin withdraw his money?

10 The cost price and selling price of peppers in a local store are shown below.

Colour	Cost price	Selling price
green	55p	80p
yellow	40p	70p
red	45p	75p

On Thursday the store manager buys 50 of each colour of pepper.

12 multipacks containing one pepper of each colour are sold for £1.90

The remaining peppers are sold individually.

At the end of the day the peppers shown below have not been sold.

Green	Yellow	Red	Multipack
2	5	3	4

Work out how much profit the store makes on the sale of peppers on that Thursday.
Show all your working out clearly.

11 n is a two digit prime number less than 15.

Find the possible pairs of m and n values

if $\dfrac{\sqrt{m}}{\sqrt{n}} = 5$.

12 The Howell family are going on a ski holiday.

They need to hire skis and jackets and must also buy ski passes.

The prices in three resort shops are shown below.

Shop A	
Ski hire	€15 per day
Ski hire (under 16)	€12 per day
Jacket	€3.50 per day
Ski pass	€20 per day or €35 for every 2 days
30% reduction for under 16 year-olds	

Shop B	
Ski hire	€90 per week
Ski hire (under 16)	€70 per week
Jacket	€26 per week
Ski pass	€130 per week
25% reduction for under 16 year-olds	

Shop C	
Ski hire	€18 per day or €44 for every 3 days
Ski hire (under 16)	€12 per day or €30 for every 3 days
Jacket	€3.50 per day or €10 for every 3 days
Ski pass	€20 per day or €56 for every 3 days $\frac{1}{3}$ reduction for under 16 year-olds

Mr and Mrs Howell have two children, aged 9 and 12.

Explain the cheapest way in which the Howell family can all hire skis, a jacket and buy a ski pass for a seven day holiday.

Give the total number of euros they must spend.

13 A factory worker works on an assembly line making magnifying glasses.

She gets £40 each day plus £5 for every 200 magnifying glasses she deals with.

During one year she works five days each week for 48 weeks. During each of these weeks she deals with an average of 1200 magnifying glasses.

She is paid an equal amount each month throughout the year. Using the tax allowance and tax rate shown below, calculate the monthly wage she receives after income tax has been deducted.

Annual personal tax allowance £8675

Tax rate 20%

14 Marcus wants to buy a camera. He tries three different stores.

Techshow
£260
$\frac{1}{5}$ off
plus special deal of a further 5% reduction
VAT included

Marleys
£165
+ VAT

E-market
4 equal payments of £59
plus 15% discount
VAT included

Which store offers the lowest price for Marcus?
Assume VAT rate is 20%. Show your working out.

15 Owen and Lucy both own some land.

During one year Owen sells $\frac{4}{9}$ of his land and is left with 40 hectares.

During the same year Lucy buys some land. Her amount of land increases by $\frac{2}{5}$ so that she now has 112 hectares.

Before the selling and buying, work out the area of Owen's land as a percentage of the area of Lucy's land.

1

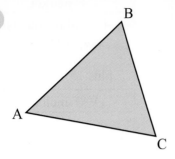

$A\widehat{B}C = 59°$

$B\widehat{A}C = 62°$

Is triangle ABC isosceles or not?
Write down your reasons clearly.

2

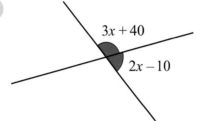

Work out the actual value of the angle $(3x + 40)°$.

> **Hint:**
> Angles on a straight line add up
> to 180°.

3

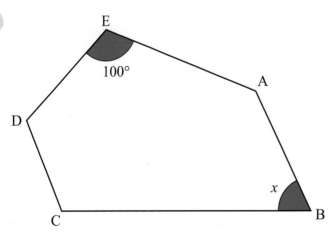

ABCDE is a pentagon.

$A\widehat{E}D = 100°$.

$B\widehat{C}D$ is 56° greater than $A\widehat{B}C$.

$C\widehat{D}E$ is treble $A\widehat{B}C$.

$B\widehat{A}E$ is equal to $C\widehat{D}E$.

Work out the value of angle x.

4

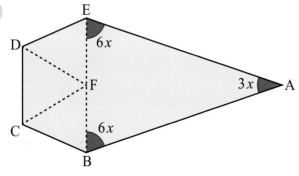

Triangles DEF, CDF and BFC
are equilateral.

Work out the actual value of $A\widehat{B}C$.

5

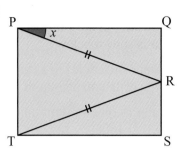

PQST is a rectangle.

PRT is an isosceles triangle.

Express angle PRT in terms of x.

Explain your reasons fully.

Hint:
$T\hat{P}R = 90 - x$

6

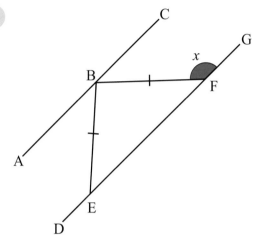

Lines AC and DG are parallel.

BE = BF

Express angle ABE in terms of x.

Show all your working.

7

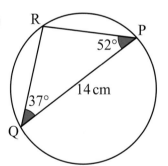

Explain *fully* why the line PQ cannot be the diameter of this circle.

8

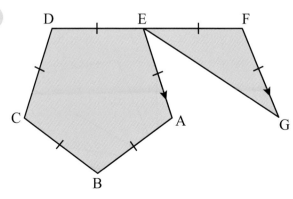

ABCDE is a regular pentagon.

EF = FG

AE is parallel to FG.

Calculate angle EGF.
Explain your reasons fully.

Hint:
Firstly find the size of an interior angle of the regular pentagon.
Next look for corresponding angles.

9

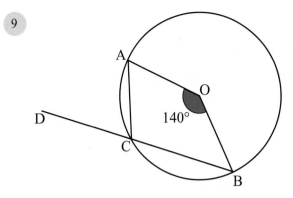

O is the centre of this circle.
Alison needs to work out the value of $\widehat{ACD}$.
Her working out is shown below.

$\widehat{ACB} = 40°$ (opposite angles in a cyclic quadrilateral add up to 180°)

$\widehat{ACD} = 140°$ (angles on a straight line add up to 180°)

Alison has made a mistake. Explain her error then work out the true value of $\widehat{ACD}$, giving all your reasons.

10

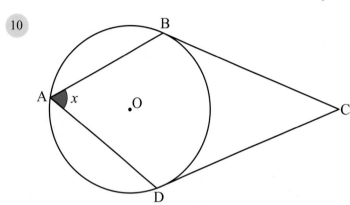

A, B and D are points on the circumference of the circle, centre O.

BC and CD are tangents to the circle.

Prove that angle BCD = 180 − 2x

Hint:
Copy the diagram and draw in the lines OB and OD.

11 The ratios of the sizes of the angles in a hexagon are 2:2:3:3:3:5
Calculate the value of the largest angle.

12 O is the centre of the circle.

Express angle BCD in terms of x.

Explain your answer fully.

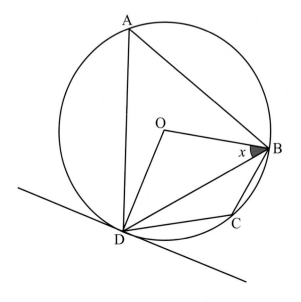

13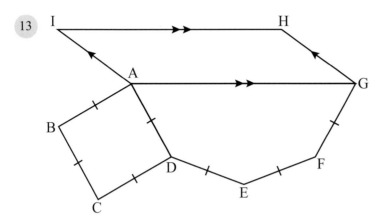

ABCD is a square.

ADEFG is half a regular octagon.

AGHI is a parallelogram.

Work out the value of $\hat{AIH}$ if $\hat{BAI} = 57\frac{1}{2}^\circ$

14 Prove that
angle OCE $= 90 - x$

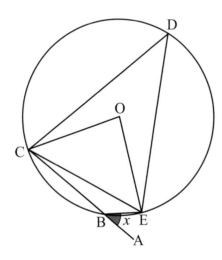

O is the centre
of the circle

15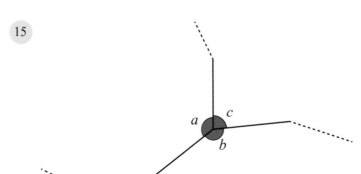

Angle a is the interior angle of a
20-sided regular polygon.

Angle b is the interior angle of a
15-sided regular polygon.

Calculate the value of angle c.

M | MIXED 2

1

ARNDALE SAVINGS
4% per annum
compound interest

Ian invests £9000 in Arndale Savings.

Eva invests £6500 in Moxon Bank.

MOXON BANK
6% per annum
compound interest

Who gets the greater amount of interest after two years and by how much?

2 $\frac{4}{7}$ of Morgan's golf balls are yellow.

$\frac{3}{8}$ of her yellow golf balls are made by Dunlop.

What percentage of all her golf balls were yellow and made by Dunlop?

3 Some of the items produced each day in a small factory are jars of carrots and peas.

The ratio of carrots to peas in each jar is 3:70.

A total of 288 carrots are used each day.
Each jar contains 280 peas.

How many jars of carrots and peas are produced each day?

Hint:
Find out how many carrots in each jar first.

4 The interior angle of a regular polygon is five times the exterior angle.
How many sides does the regular polygon have?

5

BOOTS
15% OFF
Now £66.30

BAG
35% OFF
Now £34.45

Sofia finds some boots and a bag in the Sales
but cannot afford them until she gets paid
the next day.

She goes back to the shop on the next day but
finds the deals have changed. Both the boots and
the bag now have 25% off in the Sales.
How much must Sofia now pay in total for the boots and the bag?

Hint:
Consider the 'reverse
percentage' procedure first.

6

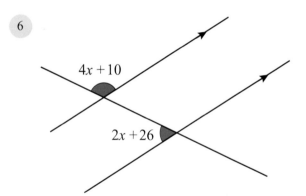

$4x + 10$

$2x + 26$

Find the value of x, hence write down the
actual values of the two angles shown.

7

1 litre
£2.20

1.5 litres
£2.90

2 litres
£3.70

The prices of freshly squeezed orange juice are shown above.

Lian needs to buy 5 litres of this orange juice.

Which cartons should she buy so that she spends the least amount of money?

Show all your working out.

8 Prove that $2^{-n} = \dfrac{1}{2^n}$

> **Hint:**
> Use $a^m \div a^n = a^{m-n}$ and remember $a^0 = 1$

9 One day 30% of the students in a college buy a meal in the canteen.

Of these students, the ratio of those who are 5 feet 8 inches tall or less to those who are over 5 feet 8 inches tall is 6:7.

The eye colour of the over 5 feet 8 inches tall students is blue, brown or other in the ratio 5:3:4 respectively.

196 of the students over 5 feet 8 inches tall do not have blue or brown eye colour.

Calculate the total number of students who attend the college.

10 After 3 years a car has lost 23% of its brand new value in 2012.

The car is worth £12 705 in 2015.

An identical car with the same brand new value in 2012 has an annual depreciation of 9% of its value at the start of each year. How much is this car worth after 3 years?

11 Timon and Sally are not allowed to use a calculator.
Timon says that $\sqrt{18} - \sqrt{8} = \sqrt{2}$
Sally says that is nonsense and that $\sqrt{18} - \sqrt{8} = \sqrt{10}$
Explain clearly who is correct, giving full justification.

12 During one year the personal tax allowance is £8975 per annum.

The tax rates are shown below.

> 20% up to £32 525 of taxable income

> 40% on taxable income above £32 525

Aubrey's annual salary is £48 825.

Blake earns a basic annual salary of £25 940 plus an additional commission payment of 15% of his basic salary.

How much more tax does Aubrey pay each month compared to Blake?

13 Prove that the exterior angle of a cyclic quadrilateral is equal to the opposite interior angle.

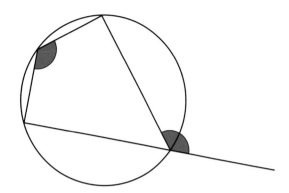

14

Larry's laptop is no longer working.

He searches the internet for a new computer.

Three deals are shown below. Which deal is the cheapest?

Explain your working out fully.

Exchange rate: £1 = €1.13

TECHPALACE	TEKNIHAUS	COMPUTERDRIVE
laptop £410 +VAT p&p free	laptop total price €440.70 plus €13.56 p&p	laptop £485 including VAT
Special offer: 20% off the total price		Sale price: $\frac{1}{5}$ off the above
		£9.50 p&p

VAT rate = 20%   p&p means 'packaging and posting'

15 Adrian and his brother want to walk $7\frac{1}{2}$ miles from their house to a pub. The brother leaves their house one hour after Adrian.

The brother has travelled $4\frac{1}{3}$ miles when Adrian is $1\frac{3}{5}$ miles from the pub.

How far is the brother behind Adrian at this instant?

A | ALGEBRA 1

1

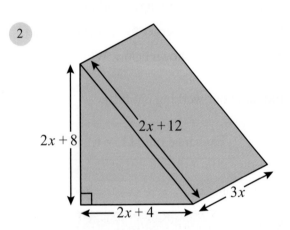

What proportion of the rectangle is red?

2

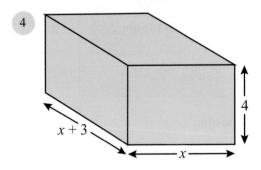

The diagram shows a prism. Show that the volume of the prism is given by the expression $6x^3 + 36x^2 + 48x$

Show your working.

> **Hint:**
> Volume of prism is the triangular area of the cross-section multiplied by its length.

3 x, y and z are integers.

Find possible values for x, y and z such that $3x + 6y + 4z$ gives a square number.

4

All measurements shown on the cuboid opposite are given in metres.
The volume of the cuboid is $216\,\text{m}^3$.

(a) Explain fully why $x^2 + 3x - 54 = 0$

(b) Write down the actual dimensions of this cuboid.

5 Simplify

$$(5x + 3)^2 - (5x - 3)^2$$

> **Hint:**
> Consider the difference of 2 squares.

6

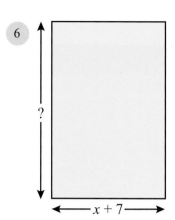

The area of this rectangle is given by the expression $(x^2 + 16x + 63)\,\text{cm}^2$

The width is $(x + 7)\,\text{cm}$ as shown.

Find an expression for the perimeter of the rectangle.

7 Tara simplifies an expression as shown below.

$$(x + 4)^2 + 6(2x + 1)$$
$$= x^2 + 16 + 12x + 1$$
$$= x^2 + 12x + 17$$

Explain very carefully each mistake that Tara has made.
What should the final answer be?

8

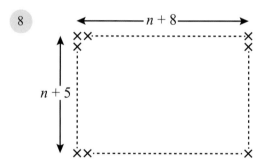

Caitlin plants $(n + 5)$ rows of cabbages.

Each row contains $(n + 8)$ cabbages.

(a) If Caitlin plants a total of 88 cabbages, prove that $n^2 + 13n - 48 = 0$

(b) Find the actual value of n.

9 The diagram shows a prism.
All measurements are in cm.
All corners are right angles.
The volume of the prism is $V\,\text{cm}^3$.

(a) Find a formula for V in terms of x.

(b) The density of this prism is y grams/cm³.
Find a formula for the mass M of the prism in terms of x and y.

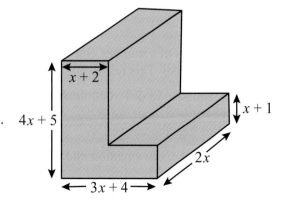

Hint:

$$\text{density} = \frac{\text{mass}}{\text{volume}}$$

10 All lengths on the rectangle opposite are
    measured in cm.

    Calculate the actual value of the perimeter
    of this rectangle.

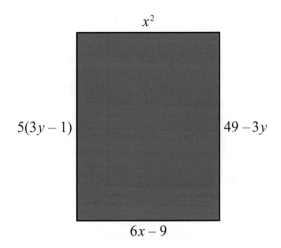

11 An expression for the area of a square is $9x^2 + 12x + 4$

    Work out an expression for the perimeter of this square.

12 A rectangular piece of card has a triangle
    cut out of it as shown opposite. The triangle
    contains a right angle. All measurements
    are in metres. The pink area is $20\,\text{m}^2$.

    (a) Show that $5x^2 - 9x - 18 = 0$

    (b) Work out the actual dimensions of the
        rectangle, giving your answers in metres.

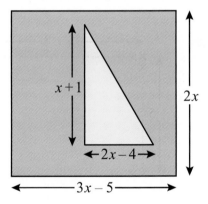

13 Arna thinks of a number. She divides 60 by her number then adds the answer to one tenth
    of her number. This results in the number 5.

    Luke thinks of a different number. He uses his number and repeats what Arna did with her
    number.
    He also gets the answer 5.

    Form a quadratic equation and solve it to find Arna's number and Luke's number.

14 $(3x + 2)(5x - a) = px^2 + qx - 8$

    Find the values of a, p and q.

15 A group of people agree to pay a total of £360 for a day's rock climbing. Each person will pay an equal share.

Four people pull out at the last moment so the remaining members of the group each have to pay an extra £3.

(a) If x is the original number of people, prove that $x^2 - 4x - 480 = 0$

(b) Find the original number of people in the group.

M	**MIXED 3**

1 Mason is a student.

45% of the total money he lives on for the year comes from a student loan. His parents give him 30% of the money.

He earns the rest of the money by delivering papers and doing bar work in the ratio 9:16.

If he earns £1200 from the bar work, how much money in total does he have to live on for the year?

2 The exchange rates in London and Berlin one day are shown opposite.

London £1 = €1.16
Berlin €1 = 87p

Evelyn is travelling from London to Berlin. She has £800 to change into euros (€).

Will she get more euros in London or Berlin?

How many more euros will she get?

3

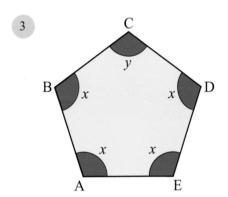

ABCDE is a pentagon.

Express y in terms of x.

Give reasons for your answer.

> **Hint:**
> Split the whole pentagon into 3 triangles first.

4 Filip needs to mix butter and flour in the ratio 1:2.

Butter costs £3.60 for 500 g.

Flour costs £1.10 for 1 kg.

Filip has £15 available to mix up a total of 4.5 kg of butter and flour.

Has he got enough money? Explain your answer fully.

5

Wheato	Wheato	Wheato
300 g	480 g	700 g
£1.44	£2.16	£3.22

The prices of three different sized boxes of cereal are shown above.
Which box offers the best value for money? You must show all your working out.

6   The relationship between temperature and volume for a gas is given by this formula

$$V_1 = \frac{V_2 T_1}{T_2}$$

What possible value for time T_2 could cause a problem with the use of this formula.
Explain your reason carefully.

7   Austin wants to invest 2000 euros in
a French bank for 2 years.
He looks at the two deals below:

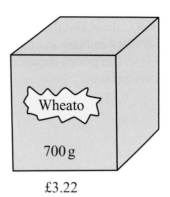

Bank de Reece
6% per annum simple interest
The bank charges a fee of 10% of the interest made when all the money is withdrawn

ZPN Bank
5% per annum compound interest

Austin will take out all the money after 2 years.

Which deal is the best for Austin and by
how much?

Hint:
The amount of simple interest
remains the same for each year.

8   Show clearly whether $(x + 4)$ is a factor of
$3x^2 + 8x + 4$

9   Mr and Mrs Callow and their two children
    want a two week holiday in one of the hotels
    shown below. The prices shown are
    the costs per person.

Pearl Hotel		
Holiday begins on	1 week	2nd week additional cost
1st Mar–20th Apr	£980	£420
21st Apr–1st Jun	£995	£425
2nd Jun–20th Jul	£1050	£470
21st Jul–31st Aug	£1175	£495
1st Sep–20th Oct	£980	£420
21st Oct–10th Nov	£995	£425
Half price for each child		
Special offer: 5% off everything if holiday is taken before August		

Canary Hotel		
Holiday begins on	1 week	2nd week additional cost
2nd Feb–27th Mar	£795	£360
28th Mar–20th May	£830	£385
21st May–15th Jul	£885	£405
16th Jul–3rd Sep	£990	£425
4th Sep–1st Nov	£865	£399
2nd Nov–31st Dec	£775	£355
One third off for each child		

Oyster Hotel		
Holiday begins on	1 week	2nd week additional cost
1st Jan–26th Mar	£915	£555
27th Mar–15th Apr	£960	£580
16th Apr–20th May	£1045	£615
21st May–19th Jul	£1120	£670
20th Jul–5th Sep	£1380	£715
6th Sep–20th Nov	£985	£590
Holiday bargain: 35% off all prices		

The Callow family want to start their
holiday on 23rd June.

Which hotel would cost the least
money for their holiday?

Write down the cost of this hotel.

Show all your working out fully.

10   $\sqrt{a^2 - b^2} = a - b$ where $a \neq 0$ and $b \neq 0$.

Is the above statement true or false?

Write down your reasons clearly.

> **Hint:**
> Try pairs of numbers or try to prove
> algebraically. Why not try both methods?

11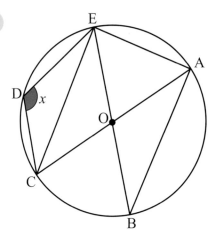

O is the centre of the circle.

Express angle BOC in terms of x.

Explain your answer fully.

12 Alexis invests £50 000 in the Cahill Building Society for 4 years and receives 3.5% per annum simple interest.

Her brother also has £50 000 to invest.
He puts it in Bentleys Bank where it receives a compound interest rate. After 4 years he has £1000 more than Alexis in his account.
What annual compound interest rate did he receive?

13 Marvin has no calculator. He decides that

$$\frac{6}{\sqrt{3}} > 2\sqrt{3}$$

Is this true or false. Give clear reasons for your answer.

14

Item	Sale % discount	Sale price	Number sold
Trousers	20	£49.60	5
Shirt	30	£26.95	7
Skirt	25	£21.75	4
Jacket	35	£54.60	4
Socks	15	£13.60	9

The sale prices of some items in a store are shown opposite. The number of each item sold one day is also shown.

Calculate the overall percentage loss of the money paid for these items on this day compared to selling the items at the pre-sale prices. Give the answer to two decimal places.

15

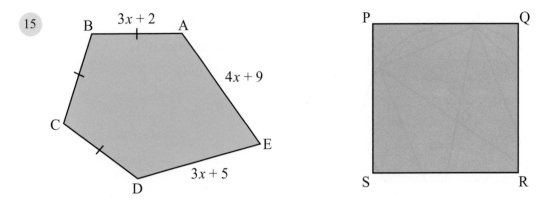

Square PQRS has a perimeter equal to the perimeter of pentagon ABCDE.

AB = BC = CD

Write down a simplified expression for the area of square PQRS.

N | NUMBER 3

1. There is a major fire in Victoria in Australia.
Planes are used to drop water on the fire.
Plane A and plane B both leave their base at 08:00.
Plane A returns to base every 50 minutes for more
water and plane B returns to base every 70 minutes
for more water.

   At what time will both planes next be back
   at their base together?

2. Three people take 4 hours to pack 2400 identical mugs into boxes.

   (a) If four people each work at the same rate as the three people, how many identical mugs
   will the four people pack into boxes in 4 hours?

   (b) Assuming they work at the same rate, how much time will be saved by eight people
   packing the 2400 identical mugs into boxes compared to just three people doing the
   packing?

3.

   0.75 m

   1.25 m

   1.25 m

   The measurements shown for the large box
   opposite are each measured to the nearest cm.

   3 cm

   3 cm

   3 cm

   Savin has thousands of little cubes of side length 3 cm,
   measured to the nearest mm.

   He wants to fill the box with as many cubes as possible.

   Calculate the greatest number of cubes that Savin might
   use and also the least possible number of cubes that he
   might use.

   Hint:
   Consider upper and
   lower bounds for
   each side length.

4. The Venn diagram opposite is used to
   find the Highest Common Factor of
   two numbers A and B.

   The Highest Common Factor is 28.

   Write down the values of the two
   numbers A and B.

   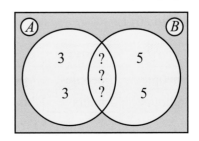

5 Proxima Centauri is the closest star to our Sun.

It is 24 900 000 000 000 miles away from the Earth.

Light travels at a speed of 3×10^8 m/s.

How many years does it take light to travel from Proxima Centauri to the Earth?

Give your answer to one decimal place.

Hint:

$$\text{speed} = \frac{\text{distance}}{\text{time}}$$

6 A bottle contains 2 litres of lemonade, measured to the nearest litre.

A carton contains 1.5 litres of orange juice, measured to the nearest tenth of a litre. Hayden is going to mix drinks of orange juice and lemonade. Each glass will contain 0.2 litres of orange juice (to the nearest 0.1 litre) and 0.25 litres of lemonade (to the nearest 0.01 litre).
What is the greatest number of glasses of orange juice and lemonade that Hayden is guaranteed to be able to make? Show all your working out clearly.

7 $4 \times 10^m + 4 \times 10^n = 400.04$

(a) Write down the possible values for m and n.

(b) What number (given in standard form) needs to be subtracted from 400.04 to give 400.039?

8 The number of people (p) in a local celebrity club trebles each year. Each person works the same number of hours each week to raise a lot of money for charity.

The total number of hours (x) worked each week is directly proportional to the number of people (p).

The total amount of money (y) raised for charity each year is directly proportional to the square of the number of hours (x) worked each week.

Complete the table below to find out how much more money is raised for charity in 2012 compared to 2011.

	2010	2011	2012
p	7 people	? people	? people
x	56 hours	? hours	? hours
y	£6272	£ ?	£ ?

9   Morgan says that $2m^2n^2$ is a factor of both $6m^2n^3$ and $10m^3n^2$.

Is this true or false? Give full reasons for your answer.

10   Ethan measures a piece of wood at 225 mm, correct to the nearest mm. Ethan uses this figure of 225 mm in a calculation. What is the maximum possible percentage error that Ethan might introduce by using this figure?

11   There are 6.3×10^5 new computers made each month.

During the same time period 2.8×10^4 old computers are destroyed.

Calculate the increase in the number of computers over a five year period.

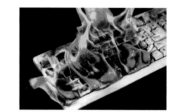

12   Angle ABC = 24°, measured correct to the nearest degree.

AC = 14 cm, measured correct to the nearest cm.

Calculate the lower and upper bounds for the area of triangle ABC, giving your answers to the nearest cm².

Hint:
You need to consider upper and lower bounds for $A\widehat{B}C$ and AC. Use trigonometry to find the length of AB.

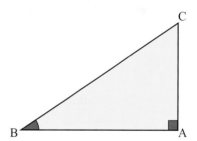

13   Teresa works at a small primary school. On her birthday she wants to give out slices of birthday cake. She needs plates and forks.

Her local store sells paper plates in boxes of fifteen at £1.99 each and packs of forty plastic forks at £2.20 each.

Teresa buys exactly the same number of plates and forks. Assuming she buys the least amount to satisfy this statement, how much does Teresa spend in total?

14   A quantity M is inversely proportional to a quantity N. The quantity N is decreased by one third of its value. Work out by what proportion quantity M will then increase by.

15   A triangular piece of wood has to be cut out as part of a shop sign. The hypotenuse of 14 cm is measured to the nearest cm. The angle of 25° is measured to the nearest degree.

What is the greatest possible value of h that may need to be used to make a triangle which fits properly onto the shop sign?

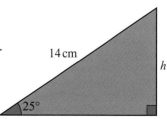

M MIXED 4

1 Cole owns an i-Phone.

He needs to choose between two possible monthly contracts as shown below.

PEACH PLAN
£35 fixed monthly payment
includes: 500 minutes phone calls Unlimited texts
Each extra minute phone call: 21.5p

NINE PLAN
£30 fixed monthly payment
includes: 400 minutes phone calls 500 free texts
Each extra minute phone call: 7.2p Each extra text: 5p

Cole looks at his phone usage in April and chooses the plan which would have cost the least amount of money. In April, Cole made 628 minutes of phone calls and 802 texts.

Which plan does Cole choose and how much cheaper would this plan have been in April compared to the other plan?

2 Savannah has some 50p and £1 coins.

The ratio of 50p coins to £1 coins is 3:5

Savannah spends £4.

The ratio of 50p coins to £1 coins is now 10:17

How many of each kind of coin did Savannah have to begin with?

3

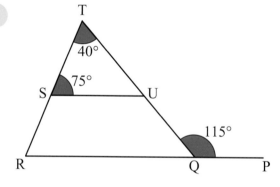

AB is a line of symmetry for this hexagon.

Express y in terms of x.

Give the answer in its simplest form.

> **Hint:**
> Split the hexagon into
> 4 triangles first.

4 Seb invests £4200 in a Building Society at 6% per annum compound interest.

At the same time Evelyn invests £6500 in a bank at 5% per annum compound interest.

How much will Evelyn have in the bank when Seb has £5620.55 in the Building Society?

5

Is QRSU a trapezium?

You must give very clear reasons
for your answer.

6

Amelia is packing for a holiday.
She packs clothes, books and other items.

$\frac{1}{18}$ of the weight is books.

$\frac{1}{6}$ of the weight is other items.

15% of the clothes are underwear.

If the underwear weighs 3.15 kg, what is the total
weight of the clothes, books and other items?

> **Hint:**
> Consider the 'reverse percentage' procedure.

7   The table opposite shows some percentage increases for a company from 2011 to 2012.

From 2011 to 2012:
Sales revenue increased by 35%
Profit increased by 24%

In 2011 the company's profit was 28% of that year's sales revenue.

Calculate the company's profit in 2012 if the 2012 sales revenue was £184 275.

8   Ben has no calculator. He needs to work out

$$7.2 \times 10^{-11} + 3.6 \times 10^{-12}$$

Explain clearly what Ben needs to do with this sum if he is to get the correct standard form answer 7.56×10^{-11}

9

Mr Garfield sells antiques at a market.
He buys 25 old toy figures at £4.50 each.
He sells 13 of the figures at £9 each.
He then reduces the price of each figure by one fifth and sells another 5.
He then reduces this new price by 20% and sells a further 4 figures.
He decides to give the remaining figures to his own children.
Calculate the overall percentage profit he made on these 25 toy figures.

10   An expression for the area of a quadrilateral is $x^2 + 7x + 12$ where $x > 0$.
Can this quadrilateral be a square? Justify your answer.

11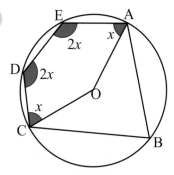

O is the centre of the circle.

Angle OAB is equal to angle OCB.

Express angle OAB in terms of x.

You must explain your working out fully.

12   A is directly proportional to the cube of B.
The value of A is 16 when B is 4.
Find the percentage increase in A when the value of B increases by 20%.

Hint:
$y = kx$ when y is directly proportional to x.

13   A rectangular box has height 12 cm.
The length of its base is equal to four times
its width plus 5 where all dimensions are
given in cm.
The volume of the box is 2772 cm³.

This box is to be filled with smaller boxes
each with dimensions 11 cm × 3 cm × 4 cm.
Work out the greatest number of these smaller
boxes which can fit into the larger box.

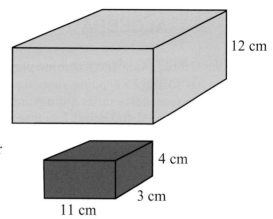

12 cm

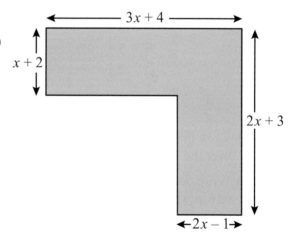

4 cm

3 cm

11 cm

14   Without using a calculator, prove that

$$\sqrt{(2\sqrt{2})^2 + (\sqrt{20})^2} = 2\sqrt{7}$$

Show all your working out clearly.

15   The area of the shape opposite is 85 cm².

(a) Explain fully why $5x^2 + 11x - 78 = 0$

(b) Work out the value of x.

$3x + 4$

$x + 2$

$2x + 3$

$2x - 1$

A   ALGEBRA 2

1 Julia, Gabriel, Aida and Kahir are playing a computer game.
Julia has scored 2500 points more than Gabriel.
Julia has scored five times more points than Aida.
Kahir has scored 400 points less than Aida.
They have all scored 12 700 points in total.
How many points has Julia scored?

Hint:
Let one of the player's scores equal n then make an equation.

2 Max is driving his car.

The graph below shows how his velocity increases steadily over a period of 20 seconds.

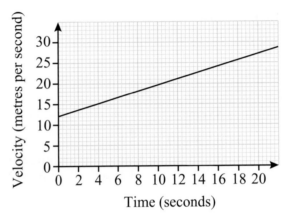

(a) Work out the rate at which the velocity increases over the 20 second period.

(b) Write down the word which usually describes the rate at which velocity changes.

Hint:
Rate of change = gradient

3 The graph of $y = x^2 - 5x + 6$ crosses the x-axis at $(2, 0)$ and $(3, 0)$.

Explain fully how the turning point (minimum) can be calculated to be at $(2.5, -0.25)$ with no sketching required.

4 Toni rearranges the equation below to make x the subject of the formula.

$$\sqrt{x - 2} + y = m$$
$$x - 2 + y^2 = m^2$$
$$x = m^2 - y^2 + 2$$

Explain clearly the mistake that Toni has made.
Show what x should equal if it is made the subject of the formula.

5

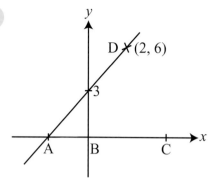

BC = 2AB

Find the equation of the line which passes though C and is parallel to the line AD.

> **Hint:**
> Find the equation of the line through A and D then use $y = 0$ to find the location of point A.

6

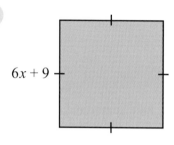

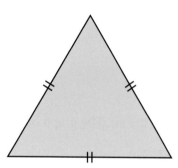

The perimeter of the square is equal to the perimeter of the equilateral triangle. If the actual value of one side of the equilateral triangle is 24 cm, find the actual area of the square.

7 (a) Draw the graph of $y = 3x^2 - x$ for values of x from $x = -3$ to $x = 3$.

(b) Write down the co-ordinates of the intercepts with the x-axis.

(c) If the turning point was reflected in the x-axis, write down its new co-ordinates.

8 Adam, Grace and Wyatt are on holiday in California in the USA. Adam has x dollars and Grace has double this amount. Adam gives 40 dollars to Grace.

Wyatt has no money so Adam now gives one third of his money to Wyatt. At the same time Grace gives one fifth of her money to Wyatt. Wyatt now has 310 dollars.

Form an equation involving x and then solve it to find out how many dollars Grace had to begin with.

9

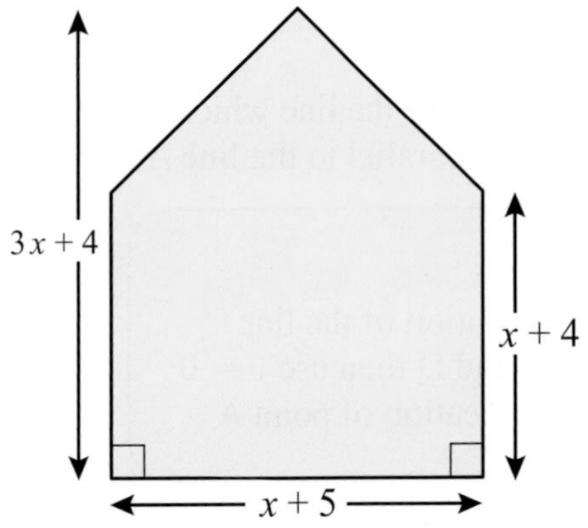

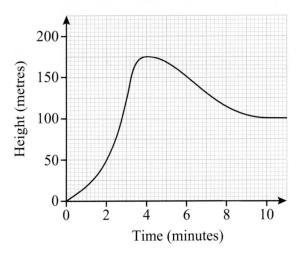

The measurements of this house are given in metres.

The total area is $36\,\text{m}^2$.

(a) Prove that $x^2 + 7x - 8 = 0$

(b) What is the actual height of the house?

10 Find the value of a if

$$\frac{18a^{\frac{1}{2}}b^3}{11ab^2} = 2b$$

11 A balloon is launched into the air. The graph below shows its height at a certain time.

(a) When is the balloon's speed equal to zero?

(b) Is the balloon travelling faster after 2 minutes or 3 minutes?
Explain your decision.

(c) Explain how you could work out the actual speed after 2 minutes.
Why would your answer probably not be accurate?

12 $f(x) = 2x + 1$ and $g(x) = \dfrac{x - 2}{3}$

If $h(x) = fg^{-1}(x)$, find the value of m when $h^{-1}(m) = m$

13

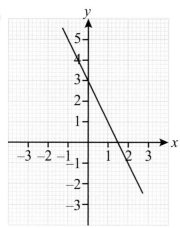

Write down the equation of any straight line which is perpendicular to the line shown opposite.

14 (a) Show that the equation $x^3 + 6x^2 - 1 = 0$ can be rearranged into the form

$$x = \sqrt{\frac{1}{x + 6}}$$

(b) Write the above equation in the form

$$x_{n+1} = \sqrt{\frac{1}{x_n + 6}}$$

Hint:
Add 1 onto both sides of the equation then factorise.

Use fixed point iteration with $x_1 = 2$ to find a value of x to 4 decimal places.

(c) The answer in part (b) is one of the roots of $x^3 + 6x^2 - 1 = 0$.
How many uses of the iterative formula in part (b) were needed before the answer was first equal to the root to 4 decimal places?

15 Hazel is a farmer. She wants to make a rectangular enclosure for her cows.

She has 64 metres of fencing and can use a wall for one side of the enclosure as shown below.

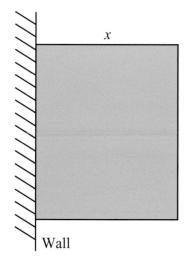

Wall

(a) Explain fully why the area A is given by the formula
$A = x(64 - 2x)$

(b) Use this formula with values of x from 0 to 32 to draw a graph showing the possible area values. (Increase the values of x by 2 each time to reduce your workload.)

(c) Use your graph to write down the maximum enclosure area which Hazel can make. Which value of x gives this maximum area?

M	**MIXED 5**

1   Kaitlyn needs to make the same cake in each of the four weeks in February.

The cake recipe for 12 people includes:

> 210 g plain chocolate
>
> 270 g icing sugar
>
> 240 g butter
>
> 6 egg whites
>
> 465 ml thick cream
>
> 195 g flour

Each week she needs to make the cake for 8 people.

She decides to buy the icing sugar, flour and plain chocolate for all the cakes at the start of February.

Each of these ingredients is sold in two sizes in her local store as shown below.

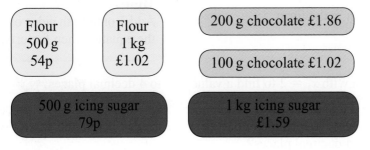

Flour
500 g
54p

Flour
1 kg
£1.02

200 g chocolate £1.86

100 g chocolate £1.02

500 g icing sugar
79p

1 kg icing sugar
£1.59

Calculate the least amount she must spend on the icing sugar, flour and plain chocolate.

2

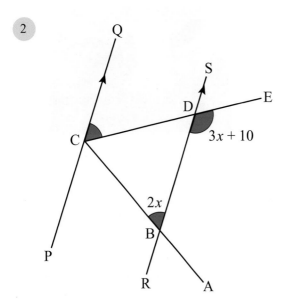

Lines PQ and RS are parallel.

Express angle QCD in terms of x.

Give reasons for your answer.

3

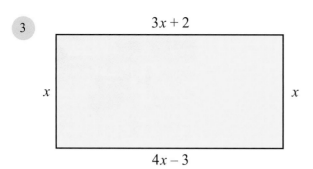

3x + 2

x   x

4x − 3

Work out the actual perimeter of this rectangle.

All measurements are given in cm.

> **Hint:**
> Opposite sides of a rectangle are equal.

4 (a) Is $2^4 \times 5^3 \times 11 \times 13$ a common multiple of 520 and 1100?
Give full reasons for your answer.

(b) If the above is a common multiple, is it the Lowest Common Multiple?
Again, give full reasons for your answer.

5 Aaron needs to buy a new bicycle machine.
He finds the machine he wants on three different store websites. The prices are shown below:

DAWSONS	RUNWELL	CYCLESTORE
£420	£499.99	£500
+ VAT	(including VAT)	15% discount then + VAT

Which store website offers the cheapest deal for Aaron if VAT is 20%? You must show all your working out.

6 n people live on Kings Street.

$\frac{4}{5}$ of these people own a car.

The following year $\frac{7}{8}$ of these people own a car.

Write down an expression in terms of n for how many more people had bought a car by the following year.

7 Hamish wants to invest £5000 for two years. Three banks offer the following deals:

EASY BANK	TRICKIER BANK	MAYBE BANK
Fixed rate 4% per annum compound interest	1st year: 3% per annum 2nd year: 5% per annum	Fixed rate 3% per annum simple interest plus bonus of £100 at the end of 2 years

Which bank should Hamish use to make the most money? Show your full working out.

44

8 There are many security cameras in a particular city.

35% of the cameras do not work.

The working cameras are found in business buildings, homes and other places in the ratio 5:1:4.

If there are 2600 working cameras in business buildings, how many security cameras are there in total in this city?

9
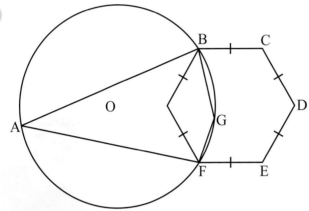

O is the centre of the circle.

OBCDEF is a regular hexagon.

Work out the value of $B\widehat{G}F$ giving full reasons for your answer.

10 If a person does not pay the year's tax bill by 31st January, a penalty payment of £100 must be made.

For every month after 31st January that the tax bill is not paid, the person will have to pay an extra 2% of the tax bill.

annual tax allowance £8744

tax rate 20%

Deven earns £2312 each month. His tax bill is calculated on this figure using the tax allowance and tax rate shown above.

How much tax must Deven pay in total if he pays the bill on 10th March?

11 Emily works out $27^{\frac{2}{3}} \div 16^{\frac{1}{4}}$ as follows:

$$27^{\frac{2}{3}} \div 16^{\frac{1}{4}} = 18 \div 4 = 4.5$$

She checks it on a calculator and it is indeed the correct answer.
Phil says she has fluked the answer and all her working out is wrong.
Who is correct?
Explain your answer carefully.

12

Two paintings have the dimensions shown above in cm.

The total area of the two paintings is 1344 cm².

The two paintings must be placed on a wall with a gap between them as shown above.

Work out the actual gap in cm.

13 Is the straight line $8x + 2y = 3$ perpendicular to the line shown opposite?

You must show all your working out.

Hint:
Two lines are perpendicular if the product of their gradients is -1.

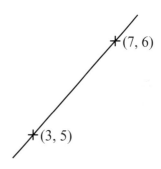

14

Mrs Hope wants to retire soon.

She has paid into a pension scheme for many years to build up a lump sum for her retirement.

When she retires, her annual pension will be at a rate equivalent to £5900 per £100 000 lump sum.

Unfortunately, during the 12 months leading up to her retirement, her lump sum is reduced by 35% because of difficult economic times.

Her lump sum at retirement is £185 900. How much less of an annual pension will she receive than if she had retired 12 months earlier?

15

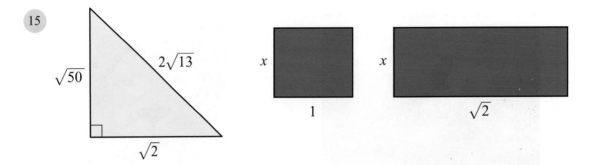

All measurements shown above are in cm.

The sum of the areas of the two rectangles is equal to the area of the triangle.

Work out the exact value of x, leaving your answer in the form $a\sqrt{b} + c$.

Do not use a calculator.

Hint:

$\dfrac{1}{a + \sqrt{b}}$ can be simplified by multiplying the numerator and denominator by $(a - \sqrt{b})$.

S | STATISTICS 1

1. A hairdresser records how long people's appointments take during the month of February. The information is shown below.

Time (to nearest minute)	0 to 15	16 to 20	21 to 25	26 to 30	over 30
Number of people	32	42	124	73	29

   (a) What is the probability that a person with a hair appointment would need 16 to 20 minutes?

   (b) 500 people come to the hairdresser during March. How many of these people would you expect to need 16 to 20 minutes?

2.  There are 12 people in a group. 7 of these people are musicians.

   3 of the people leave the group.

   Find the probability that at least two of these 3 people were musicians.

   Hint:
   Create a probability tree.

3. John visits a sports shop. There are 20 different football club shirts, 10 different coloured shorts and 7 different coloured socks. John can afford to buy either a shirt and shorts or a shirt and socks or shorts and socks. How many different combinations of shirts, shorts or socks are available to John?

4. There are some yellow and black beads in a bag.
   One bead is removed from the bag then replaced. Another bead is then removed.
   The probability of removing two black beads is $\frac{16}{49}$.
   What originally was the probability of removing one yellow bead?

5. Lauren has a box of paper clips. The number of each colour is shown below.

Colour	Frequency
Pink	8
Yellow	2
Green	5
Blue	16
Red	5

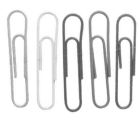

   Lauren randomly takes three paper clips. Work out the probability that all three paper clips are the same colour.

6 There is a 58% chance that a seventeen year-old has a GCSE Maths grade of 5 or above.

There is a 66% chance that a seventeen year-old has a GCSE English grade of 5 or above.

If a seventeen year-old is chosen at random, what is the probability that this person will have a grade C or above in Maths or English but not both?

7 (a)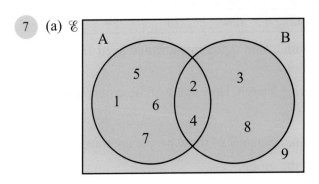

Use the Venn diagram opposite to determine
which statement below is correct:

(i) $n(A \cap B') > n(B)$
(ii) $n(A \cap B') = n(B)$
(iii) $n(A \cap B') < n(B)$

Give reasons for your answer.

(b) Copy the Venn diagram opposite
then shade the region given by $A \cup B'$

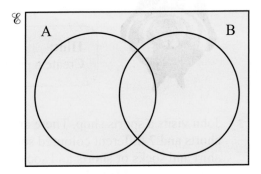

(c) Write down different set notation which represents
the same region to that given in part (b).

Hint:
Consider the region
given by $A' \cap B$ first.

8 There are five Europeans, six Americans and seven Africans on a Languages Course at a College. Calculate the probability that the first three people to arrive at College one day will all be European or will all be African.

9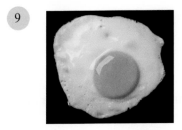

Ethan arrives late at a supermarket café.
The only remaining breakfast items are 2 fried eggs, 8 rashers of bacon and 10 sausages. He may choose three items at random for 99p.

Work out the probability that he chooses two fried eggs and one rasher of bacon.

10 80 people were asked whether they like Coronation Street or Eastenders.

8 people said they like Coronation Street only.
20 people said they like Eastenders only.
30 people said they do not like either.

(a) Complete a Venn diagram for the above information.

(b) If one person is chosen at random, what is the probability of the person liking both Coronation Street and Eastenders?

(c) Given that a person likes Eastenders, what is the probability that the person likes Coronation Street also?

11  Alex has n eggs. 5 of these eggs are cracked.

Alex chooses two eggs at random.

The probability that both of these eggs will be cracked is $\frac{1}{30}$.

(a) Prove that $n^2 - n - 600 = 0$

(b) How many eggs did Alex actually have to begin with?

12 Each person at a school plays at least one of hockey or netball. 81% play hockey and 65% play netball.

(a) Copy and complete the Venn diagram opposite.

(b) One person is chosen at random.
    Find the probability that this person
    (i) played hockey given that they played netball.
    (ii) played hockey given that they only played one of the sports.

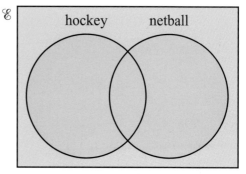

13 Sheldon has a take-away meal each Friday night.
The probability of choosing an Indian meal is 0.3
The probability of choosing a Chinese meal is 0.5
The probability of choosing a Thai meal is 0.2
Work out the probability that on the first two Fridays in May, Sheldon chooses meals from the same nation.

14 There are 52 playing cards in a pack.
26 of the cards are red and the remainder
are black.

If 3 cards are randomly taken from the pack,
work out the probability that at least one of
the cards will be red.

15 A bag contains n balls. There are m red balls and the remainder are blue.

If two balls are removed from the bag, find an algebraic
expression for the probability of removing one of
each colour. Write the answer in simplified form.

Hint:
Create a probability tree with the initial
number of blue balls being $(n - m)$.

M | MIXED 6

1   On 1st September 2011, Brooklyn takes out a mortgage of £70 000 at a fixed rate of 4.14% per annum. The fixed rate deal lasts for 5 years. The bank calculates the interest on what is owed on the last day of each year of the mortgage then adds it on to the debt.

If Brooklyn pays the money back early, she has to pay a penalty as shown below:

Pay back within:	Penalty (% of amount owing)
1 year	5%
2 years	4%
3 years	3%
4 years	2%
5 years	1%

Brooklyn pays back a fixed amount of £842 at the end of each month.

She inherits some money and is able to pay back all the amount owing on 31st August, 2014.

Assuming that the interest has been added and the August monthly payment has been made, how much of a penalty does Brooklyn have to pay?

2   Calculate the area of this picture if the perimeter is 86 cm.

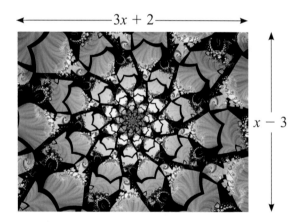

$3x + 2$

$x - 3$

3   The ratios of dogs to cats in a kennel is 5:3 on Friday, 3:2 on Saturday and 5:4 on Sunday. Mason records the number of animals in the kennel on these days below.

Day	Number of dogs and cats
Friday	24
Saturday	30
Sunday	35

Mason has made a mistake in his records on one of the days. Which day?
Explain your reason carefully.

4 Renata parks her car in a city supermarket car park.

The first $1\frac{1}{2}$ hours are free of charge.

After that, Renata has to pay 60p for every 20 minutes or part of 20 minutes.

How much does Renata pay if she arrives at 1:15 p.m. and leaves the car park at 4:30 p.m.?

5 The probability tree opposite is drawn to represent a situation. a, b, c, d, e, f and g are probabilities.

Explain clearly why $a + b = c + d + e = f + g = 1$

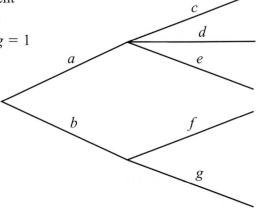

6

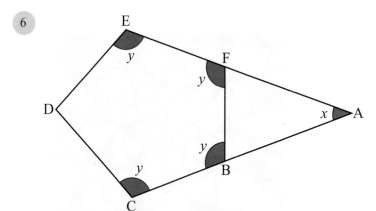

AF = AB
Express angle CDE
in terms of x.

Hint:
Maybe cut the pentagon into triangles to find the sum of the angles in a pentagon.

7

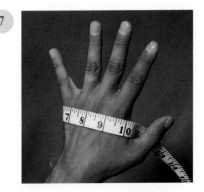

Paige has a piece of ribbon. She uses $\frac{2}{5}$ of the ribbon on a present for her mother and another $\frac{1}{3}$ of the ribbon on a gift for her sister.

She has 52 cm of ribbon left over.

How long was the piece of ribbon to begin with?

8 x and y are integers such that

$$x^{\frac{2}{3}} = y^{\frac{1}{3}}$$

Write down all the possible pairs of values of x and y if x is a factor of 14.

9

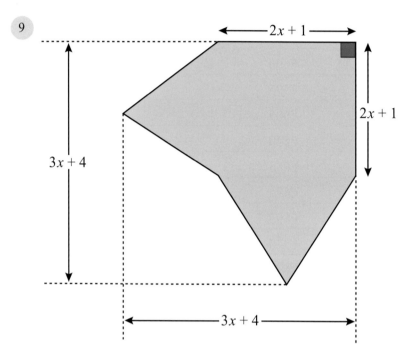

Show that the area of the blue shape can be written as $6x^2 + 11x + 4$

(The blue shape is made from a square and two triangles.)

10 (a) Show that the equation

$$(2x + 3)^2 - 2x(x + 3) - (x + 1)^2 = 4$$

can be simplified to the form $x^2 + ax + b = 0$
where a and b are to be stated clearly.

(b) Find the co-ordinates of the turning point
of the graph of $y = x^2 + ax + b$

Hint:
Make a table of values for
$y = x^2 + ax + b$ when a
and b have been found.

11 Mr and Mrs Williams wish to take a holiday at the Hotel Magnifique.
They have one child. The prices (in euros) are shown below.

HOTEL MAGNIFIQUE		
Depart on:	7 night price per adult for bed and breakfast	
9 Apr–17 May	€540	ADD 35% FOR FULL BOARD
18 May–30 Jun	€585	
1 Jul–31 Aug	€690	
1 Sep–17 Oct	€595	
18 Oct–6 Nov	€605	
7 Nov–20 Dec	€540	CHILD PRICE: 85% OF ADULT PRICE
21 Dec–4 Jan	€685	
5 Jan–16 Feb	€575	
17 Feb–2 Mar	€595	
3 Mar–8 Apr	€520	

OCTOBER DEAL

15% OFF ALL PRICES

The Williams family want to go to the hotel on 15th July for 7 nights bed and breakfast or on 10th October for 7 nights full board.

(a) Which holiday will be cheaper and by how much?

(b) How much will the cheaper holiday cost in pounds if the exchange rate below is used?

£1 = €1.13

12 Tyler is given a function $f(x) = 5x - 3$
He is asked to find the value of x when $f(x) = f^{-1}(x)$.
His working out is shown below.

$$f(x) = f^{-1}(x)$$
$$5x - 3 = \frac{x - 3}{5}$$
$$25x - 15 = x - 3$$
$$24x = 12$$
$$x = \tfrac{1}{2}$$

Tyler has made an error. Identify the error then find the correct value of x.

13

 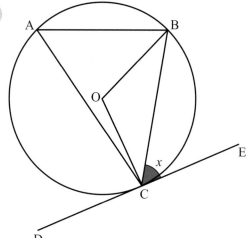

O is the centre of the circle.

Prove that angle BAC = x

This will prove the alternate segment theorem.

14 Prove that

$$\frac{(3 - \sqrt{3})(3 + \sqrt{3})}{2\sqrt{3}} = \sqrt{3}$$

15 A quantity P is inversely proportional to a quantity Q.
Q is directly proportional to the square of a quantity M.

$Q = 36$ when $M = 3$.

$P = 6$ when $M = 2$.

Find the value of M when $P = \frac{2}{3}$.

Show all your working out clearly.

Hint:
Remember to use the constant of proportionality, e.g. if y is inversely proportional to x then

$$y = \frac{k}{x}$$

M | MIXED 7

1

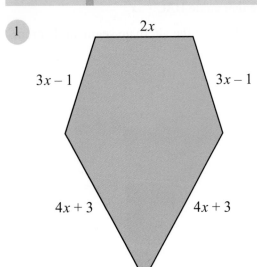

2x

3x − 1   3x − 1

4x + 3   4x + 3

The perimeter of this pentagon is 52 cm.

What is the actual length of the longest side of this pentagon?

Give your answer in cm.

2 Leah makes ornaments from shells.

$\frac{2}{3}$ of the shells are used to make the outer three rings.

The ratio of shells used in the outer three rings is 9:11:15 moving from inside to outside.

If Leah uses 60 shells for the outside ring, how many shells does she use to make seven complete ornaments?

Explain your working fully.

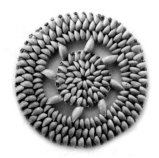

3 Mariah and Jackson rearrange a formula as shown below to make x the subject of the formula.

Mariah's solution

$mx - am = b$

$m(x - a) = b$

$x - a = \dfrac{b}{m}$

$x = \dfrac{b}{m} + a$

Jackson's solution

$mx - am = b$

$mx = b + am$

$x = \dfrac{b + am}{m}$

They both think the other person is wrong. Who do you think is correct? Comment fully on their solutions.

4   Chocolates
    4.14 euros
    250 g

Exchange rate
£1 = 1.15 euros

Maurice is in Bruges and buys the Belgium chocolates shown opposite.

When he gets back to England, he finds $\frac{1}{2}$ kg of the same type of chocolates being sold for £7.76.

In which country were the chocolates better value for money, Belgium or England?

Show all your working out.

5   (a) $n^{\frac{1}{2}} \times n^{\frac{1}{2}} = n^{\frac{1}{2} + \frac{1}{2}}$

$(n^{\frac{1}{2}})^2 = n$

$n^{\frac{1}{2}} = \sqrt{n}$

The working out opposite shows that the index $\frac{1}{2}$ means square root.

Repeat this process to show that the index $\frac{1}{3}$ means cube root.

(b) Simplify $(27m^6n^9)^{\frac{1}{3}}$

6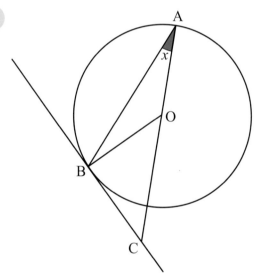

O is the centre of the circle.

BC is a tangent to the circle.

Express angle ACB in terms of x.

Give all the reasons leading to your answer.

7   Last year Liam paid £2592 tax.
    At the end of the year he was given a 4% pay increase.

What is his current salary?

Last year's personal tax allowance and tax rate are shown below.

Tax allowance £9250

Tax rate 20%

Hint:
Think about the 'reverse percentage' process.

8

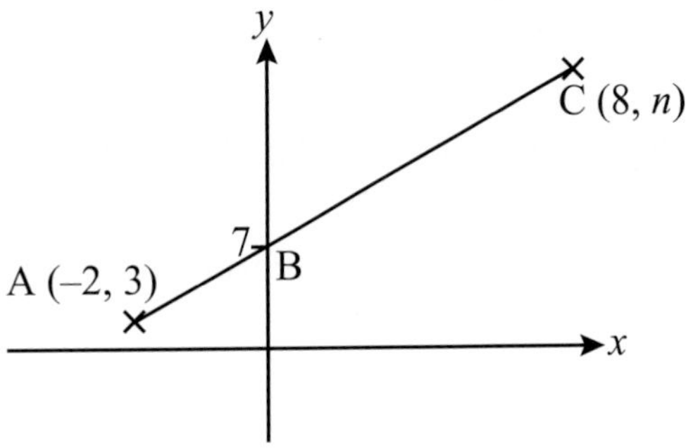

AB:BC = 1:4

Work out the value of *n*.

9 (a) Work out the quarterly electricity bill from Electrogen shown below.

previous reading: 20178 units
present reading: 21613 units
The first 950 units cost 12.184p per unit
Remaining units over 950 cost 9.718p per unit
VAT is added at 5%

(b) The same household are offered the following electricity deal from the Cotswold Electricity Company.

£12 per month fixed fee
All units cost 9.23p per unit
VAT is added at 5%

Would this household have paid more or less for the electricity used in part (a) if the Cotswold Electricity Company had been chosen?

Find the difference between the two bills.

10 The Lobster Shack restaurant has 4 starters, 8 main meals and 4 desserts on offer.

The Old Hare restaurant has 3 starters, 6 main meals and 4 desserts on offer.

A starter, main meal or dessert are each known as a course.

A person may choose 1 course, 2 courses or 3 courses as a meal.

How many more different meal choices would there be at the Lobster Shack compared to the Old Hare?

11 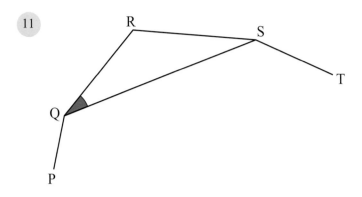 PQRST is part of a regular polygon with n sides.

(a) Express angle RQS in terms of n.

(b) Find the actual value of angle RQS when $n = 60$.

12 The current velocity v of a particle is given by the formula $v = u + at$ where u is the initial velocity, a is the acceleration and t is the time taken.

u, a and t for particles P and Q are shown below.

Particle P
$u = 2$ m/s (to nearest whole number)
$a = 6$ m/s^2 (to nearest whole number)
$t = 5$ s (to nearest whole number)

Particle Q
$u = 2.6$ m/s (to nearest tenth)
$a = 5$ m/s^2 (to nearest whole number)
$t = 6.4$ s (to nearest tenth)

What is the maximum possible difference in the current velocities of particles P and Q?

Hint:
Consider upper and lower bounds.

13 Lena wants to go on a city break for four nights.

She will choose the cheapest of the 3 deals shown below.

Which deal will she choose if she pays by credit card?

Explain your reasons fully.

Jaga Tours	
3 nights plus travel	£269
Each extra night	£58
City taxes per night	£6.50
Credit card payment: 2.5% extra charge	

Easy Stay	
4 nights plus travel	£342
City taxes	£26
Deal price: 5% off	
Credit card payment: 3.5% extra charge	

Sunny Places	
Each night (all city taxes included)	£64
Travel	£118
Deal price: $\frac{1}{10}$ off	
Credit card payment: 1% extra charge	

14 80 people are staying in a hotel.

Some people swim at the hotel.

21 people have an evening meal at the hotel.

Twice as many people do not swim or have a meal compared to the number of people who swim.

Given that a person has an evening meal, the probability that the person swims is $\frac{1}{3}$.

If a person is chosen at random, work out the probability that the person swims.

> **Hint:**
> Draw a Venn diagram.

15

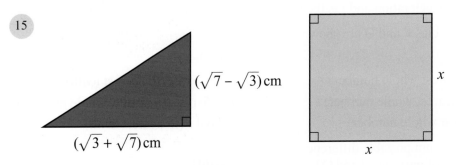

$(\sqrt{7} - \sqrt{3})\,\text{cm}$

$(\sqrt{3} + \sqrt{7})\,\text{cm}$

x

x

Find the exact value of x if the area of the square is equal to the area of the triangle.

PART TWO

M | MIXED 8

1 Aidan wants to bake enough bakewell tarts for 70 people.

The recipe for the pastry is shown below.

Pastry (for 8 people)

125 g plain flour

75 g butter

25 g sugar

1 egg

Aidan buys all the plain flour in 500 g bags. If he buys the least number of bags, how much plain flour will he have left when he has made enough bakewell tarts?

2

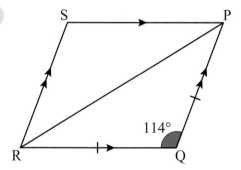

(a) Triangle PQR is isosceles.
Prove that triangle PRS is isosceles.

(b) Name the quadrilateral PQRS.
Give reasons for your answer.

3 The volume of this cuboid is 192 cm³.

Show that $x^2 + 4x = 44$ then use trial and improvement to find the value of x correct to one decimal place.

You must show all your working out.

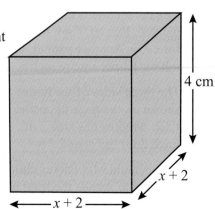

4 cm

$x + 2$

$x + 2$

4 A farmer has some fields which make a large square.

If the large square was all planted with wheat, the farmer would make £25 440 profit.

If the large square had nothing planted in it, the government would pay the farmer £4152.

The farmer plants some wheat (green area) and leaves some land with nothing planted on it (yellow area).

Work out how much the farmer will make in total.

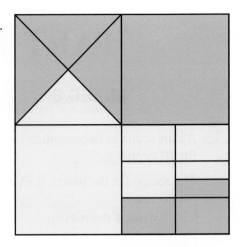

5 (a) Explain what the symbol '≡' means.

(b) Prove that $(x - 1)(2x + 2)(6x - 3) \equiv (x + 1)(4x - 2)(3x - 3)$

6

TRISTAR BUILDING SOCIETY	THAMES BANK
0.4% per month compound interest	4.9% per annum compound interest
The interest is added at the end of each month	The interest is added at the end of each year

Maya has £20 000 to invest for two years.

Which of the two accounts above should Maya choose so that she makes the most money? How much more money will she make after two years by using this account compared to using the other one?

7 Mrs Parker wants three sides of her house to be painted. Painter, Carl, offers to do the whole job for £450. Another painter, Helen, offers to do the job for £3 per square metre.

The three sides of the house to be painted are shown on the page opposite.
Each window has area 2 m².
Each door has area 2.5 m².

Who should Mrs Parker choose to paint her house so that she spends the least amount of money? How much cheaper is this painter?

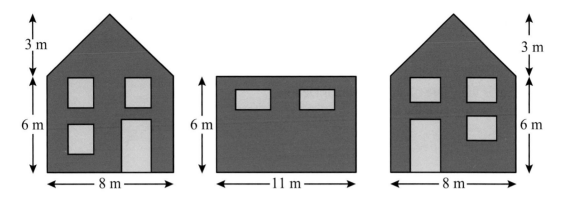

8   Mrs Thomas needs help at home. A nurse visits every 6 days and a social worker visits every 8 days.

The nurse and social worker both visit on July 19th. On what date will both the nurse and social worker next visit Mrs Thomas on the same day?

9

Three friends have a total of 23 euro coins.

Max has x coins.

Zoe has twice as many coins as Max.

Lily has 5 coins less than Max.

How many coins does Lily have?

Hint:
Form an equation, in terms of x, from the given information.

10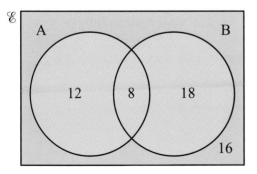

Explain *fully* why
$p((A \cup B)') = \frac{8}{27}$

11 Debbie is creating a lawn in the shape shown opposite.

The arrows indicate two parallel lines.

What is the value of angle x which Debbie must use to make the lawn?

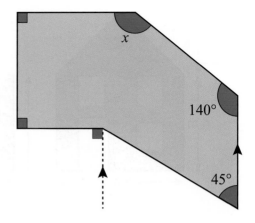

140°

45°

12 In the Olympic Games one year, Great Britain wins 10% of all the medals in the ratio 5:4:7 for gold, silver and bronze respectively.

Great Britain actually wins 24 silver medals.

In the same Olympic Games, USA win 15% of all the medals in the ratio 9:7:8 for gold, silver and bronze respectively.

How many silver medals did USA win?

13

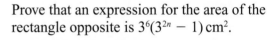

$27(3^n - 1)$ cm

$9(3^{n+1} + 3)$ cm

Prove that an expression for the area of the rectangle opposite is $3^6(3^{2n} - 1)$ cm².

Hint:
$a^m \times a^n = a^{m+n}$

14

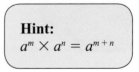

O is the centre of the circle.
Express angle OBD in terms of x.
Explain your reasons fully.

15 The velocity–time graph below shows Beth's velocity (v) and time (t) during a cycling race.

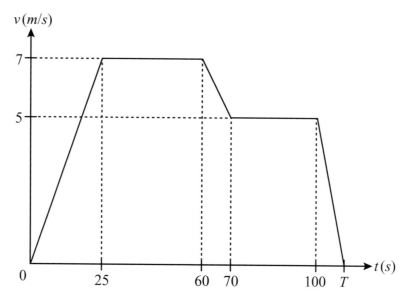

The race is exactly 600 m long.

Beth wanted to finish the race in under 2 minutes.

Did she succeed or not?

Justify your answer with full working out.

Hint:
The area under the curve on a velocity–time graph is equal to the distance travelled.

G | GEOMETRY 2

1

A ladder is leaning against a wall as shown opposite.

Stella climbs up the ladder 1.3 m from the bottom. At this point, how high above the ground are the soles of her feet?
Give the answer to one decimal place.

Diagram: right-angled triangle with vertical side 3.5 m and horizontal base 2.3 m.

2

The triangular metal prism opposite stands on a table.

The prism can stand on any of its 5 faces.

On which face would it stand when exerting the greatest pressure on the table. You must fully justify your answer.

Hint:
$$\text{pressure} = \frac{\text{force}}{\text{area}}$$

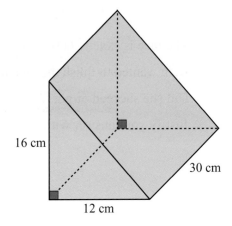

16 cm

30 cm

12 cm

3

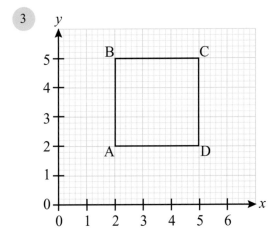

Square ABCD opposite is reflected in the line $y = x$ followed by a 90° clockwise rotation such that all the points forming one side only of the original square remain invariant.

(a) What are the possible centres of rotation?

(b) In each case, state which points remain invariant.

Hint:
An invariant point means its position is left unchanged by the transformation.

4   A group of research scientists earn the money shown below.

Name	Pay rate per hour
Cameron	£7.90
Oliver	£7.90
Diya	£12.40
Tom	£8.26
Chun	£9.75
Lucy	£14.25

The shaded parts of the table below show how many hours each person worked for last Tuesday.

Name	0800	0900	1000	1100	1200	1300	1400	1500	1600	1700	1800	1900	2000
Diya													
Tom													
Lucy													
Cameron													
Alice													
Oliver													
Chun													

Time and a half is paid for any work after 7 p.m.

The ratio of Tom's total pay to Alice's total pay for last Tuesday is 4:5.

Calculate Alice's pay rate per hour if she finished work at exactly 3:15 p.m.

5

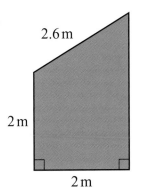

2.6 m

2 m

2 m

1 m

The diagram above shows a side view of Pete's shed with some dimensions indicated.

Pete is 1.8 m tall and can reach up to 0.5 m above his head.
He stands on a 1 m high stool.

Can he reach the highest point of the shed? You must give all your reasons fully.

6

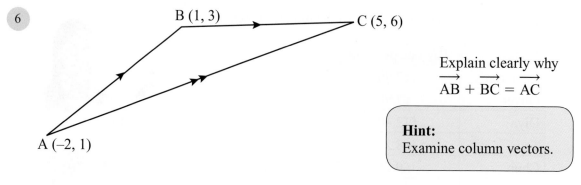

B (1, 3)

C (5, 6)

A (−2, 1)

Explain clearly why
$$\overrightarrow{AB} + \overrightarrow{BC} = \overrightarrow{AC}$$

Hint:
Examine column vectors.

7

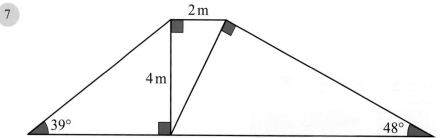

2 m

4 m

39°

48°

The steel framework for part of a roof is shown above.
Each side of each triangle is a steel girder.
Calculate the total length of steel that is required for this framework.
Give your answer to one decimal place.

8

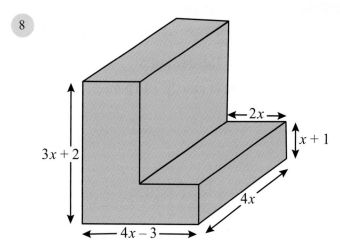

$2x$

$x + 1$

$3x + 2$

$4x$

$4x − 3$

All dimensions shown for this prism are measured in cm.

The prism is made of material with density 8 g/cm³.

Write down an expression, in terms of x, for the mass of the prism.

9 Prove that an expression for the length of a diagonal in the square opposite is $x\sqrt{2}$ cm by using (a) Pythagoras and (b) trigonometry. *Do not use a calculator.*

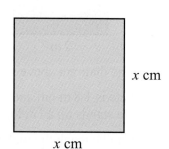

x cm

x cm

10

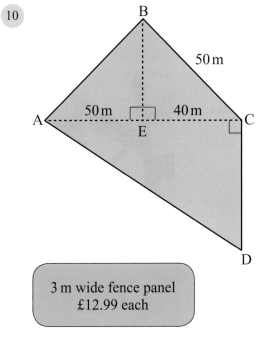

A farmer wants to put fencing completely around the field shown opposite. The length CD is equal to the length AC.

Each outer edge of the field will be fenced using 3 m wide fence panels. Parts of a fence panel cannot be used on more than one side of the field.

What is the least amount the farmer will have to pay for all the fence panels?

3 m wide fence panel
£12.99 each

11

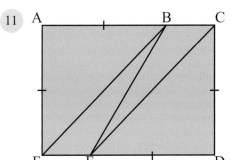

ACDF is a rectangle.

Triangle ABF is isosceles.

Triangle CDE is isosceles.

Prove that triangles BEF and BCE are congruent.

12

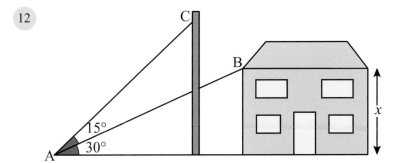

Mr Higgins attaches a rope from a point A to a point B on his house x metres above the ground. He wants to fix Christmas lights to this rope which has length h metres.

He attaches another rope from a point A to a point C on a flagpole. The length AB is equal to the length AC.

Find the height of C above the ground in terms of x.

13 Leah and her friend visit London.
They decide to do a city bus tour then go to the cinema.
They arrive at a train station which is 2 km from the start
of the city bus tour. They walk from the train station to
this bus starting point at a speed of 400 m every 5 minutes.

The city bus tour lasts for one hour twenty-five minutes.
The starting times are shown below.

City Bus Tours
Leave at quarter to and quarter past every hour

It takes 5 minutes to walk from the end of the bus tour to
the cinema. The film showing times are shown below.

Film showing times
14:15, 16:20, 18:00,
19:10, 20:30, 21:05
Film duration: 2 hours 12 minutes

Leah's dad agrees to drive and pick them up from outside the cinema at 7:30 p.m. and no later.

(a) If they watch the latest film possible, how long will they have to wait for Leah's dad
after the film has finished?

(b) If they watch this film, what is the latest time they can leave the train station to ensure
that they fit in the city bus tour?

14 Prove that
$$(1 + \sin 60°)(1 - \cos 30°) = \sin^2 30°$$
Do not use a calculator.

> **Hint:**
> $\sin^2 30°$ means $(\sin 30°)^2$

15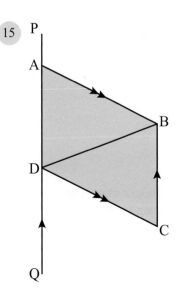

PQ is parallel to BC.

AB is parallel to DC.

Prove that triangles ABD and BCD are congruent.

M | MIXED 9

1. Julie lives in Peckford. She wants to spend two hours ice skating in Tenby and at least one-and-a-half hours having a meal and drink afterwards. A bus timetable from Hatton to Tenby is shown below.

Hatton	0950	1030	1130	1230	1330	1430	1450	1530	1550
Marby	1013	1053	1153	1253	1353	1453	1513	1553	1613
Peckford	1025	1105	1205	1305	1405	1505	1525	1605	1625
Neane	1047	1127	1227	1327	1427	1527	1547	1627	1647
Tenby	1105	1145	1245	1345	1445	1545	1605	1645	1705

A bus timetable from Tenby to Hatton is shown below.

Tenby	1535	1635	1735	1835	1935	2035	2135	2235	2305
Neane	1554	1654	1754	1854	1954	2054	2154	2254	2324
Peckford	1616	1716	1816	1916	2016	2116	2216	2316	2346
Marby	1628	1728	1828	1928	2028	2128	2228	2328	2358
Hatton	1650	1750	1850	1950	2050	2150	2250	2350	0020

Tenby ice skating sessions		
Open		
1100	to	1330
1430	to	1700
1800	to	2030

Julie takes 10 minutes to walk from her home to the Peckford bus stop.

She takes 25 minutes to walk from Tenby Bus Station to the ice skating centre.

The table opposite shows when ice skating is possible.

(a) If Julie leaves her home at 1245, what is the earliest bus she might want to catch home from Tenby?

(b) If she catches this bus, what time should she arrive home?

Show all your working out fully.

2.

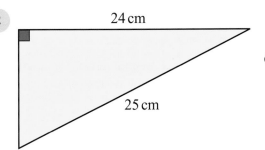

Calculate the area of this triangle.

3 A square is enlarged by factor $-k$ about the point (a, b) where k, a and b are integers.
The same transformation could be achieved by doing two separate transformations.
Describe fully these two separate transformations.

Hint:
Draw a diagram and trial some numbers for k, a and b.

4 The Henton travel agents sell and buy euros.

One day they have the following deal.

We buy at
€1.12 = £1

We sell at
£1 = €1.06

Martin changes £350 into euros. Unfortunately his firm then tells him that he cannot be released for his holiday. He takes the euros back to Henton travel agents and changes them back into pounds.

How much of his original money does he lose?

5

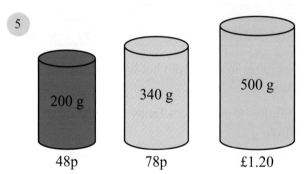

200 g   340 g   500 g

48p   78p   £1.20

The prices of three tins of baked beans are shown opposite.

Which tin gives the best value?

Explain your answer fully.

6

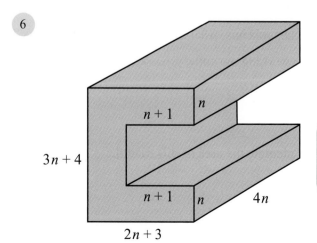

$n + 1$ n

$3n + 4$

$n + 1$ n $4n$

$2n + 3$

All measurements are in cm.

Find an expression in terms of n for the volume of this prism.

Simplify your answer as much as possible.

Hint:
Volume of a prism is cross-sectional area multiplied by its length.

7 The velocity v of a particle after time t is given by the formula

$$v = 7 - 3t$$

where v is measured in m/s and t in seconds.

(a) Is the particle speeding up or slowing down ?
    Give clear reasons for your answer.

(b) Write down the value of the particle's acceleration
    or deceleration. Give clear reasons for your answer.

(c) Write down the correct units for your answer to part (b).

Hint:
Relate to $y = mx + c$

8

It is estimated that in one area of the UK there are two million mice and 600 000 cats.

Each year the number of mice decreases by 3% of the population at the start of the year.

Each year the number of cats increases by 5% of the population at the start of the year.

Calculate the number of cats when the mice population has reduced to 1 825 346.

9 A History exam paper has three sections A, B and C. Section A consists of 3 questions, section B has 5 questions and there are 5 questions in section C.

A student may choose 1 question from section A, 2 questions from section B and 2 questions from section C or 2 questions from section A, 1 question from section B and 2 questions from section C.
In how many different ways can a student choose the questions for this exam paper?

10 Explain clearly why $\sqrt{80} - \sqrt{20} = \sqrt{20}$
   Do *not* use a calculator.

11 Angle x opposite is the interior angle
   of a regular polygon with n sides.

   Express x in terms of n.

   Give reasons for your answer.

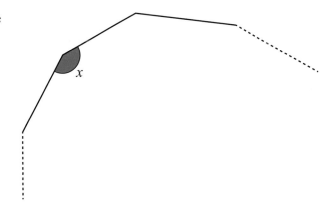

12

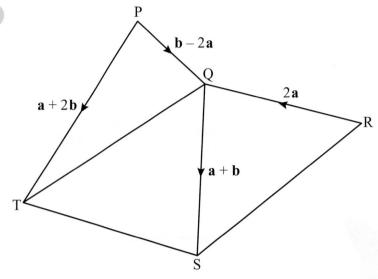

Use vectors to prove that QRST in the diagram above is a parallelogram.

13 Calculate the values of x and h.

Give each answer to one decimal place.

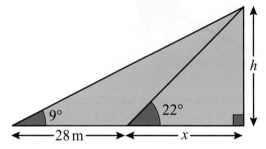

14 A function $f(x) = 2x + 3$ and a function $g(x) = 3x + 2$
Eve has to solve the equation $gf(x) = f^{-1}g(x)$
Her solution is shown below:

$$y = 2x + 3 \Rightarrow \frac{y - 3}{2} = x \Rightarrow f^{-1}(x) = \frac{x - 3}{2}$$

$$gf(x) = f^{-1}g(x) \Rightarrow 2(3x + 2) + 3 = 3\left(\frac{x - 3}{2}\right) + 2$$

$$6x + 7 = \frac{3x - 9}{2} + 2$$

$$12x + 10 = 3x - 9$$

$$9x = -19$$

$$x = -\frac{19}{9}$$

Barney says the answer should be $x = -\frac{23}{9}$

Has Eve made an error and, if so, explain clearly what mistake was made.

15

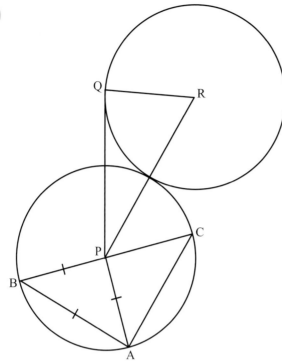

Two identical circles touch as shown opposite.

P and R are the centres of the two circles. PQ is a tangent to the circle with centre R.
Triangle ABP is equilateral.

Prove that triangles ABC and PQR are congruent.

S STATISTICS 2

1   Diego asked some people what their
    favourite food was.

    His findings are shown in the table.

Type of meal	Frequency
Chinese	12
Indian	15
Italian	8
Thai	3
Other	2

Represent this information in a suitable diagram or chart.

2   125 students in Year 9 study French, German or Spanish.

    22 girls study French. There are 70 girls in total. 25 boys do German.
    There are 42 students doing Spanish, of which 12 are boys.

    How many students in total study German?

    Hint:
    Create a two-way
    table.

3   Angelina wants to find out what type of music the
    people in her tutor group at school like best.

    Design a data collection sheet that Angelina can use
    to collect this information.

4   The charts below show how many students studied History, Geography and Art in
    Lanchester High School in the years shown.

Year 2016

	Male	Female	Total
History	32	40	72
Geography	45	35	80
Art	58	70	128
Total	135	145	280

Work out the percentage increase in the
number of students taking Geography in
2017 compared to 2016.

Year 2017

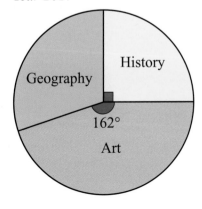

An increase
of $\frac{1}{7}$ in the
total number
of students
compared to
2016.

5 A certain make of car cost £11 500 when it was brand new.

The values of some cars of this make are recorded in the years that follow.

The values are shown on the scatter graph below.

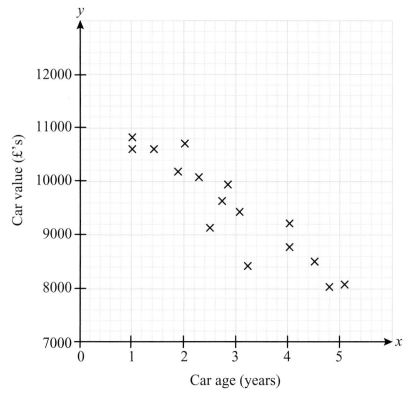

Car age (years)

(a) Describe the relationship between the car value and the car age.

(b) Copy the scatter graph then estimate the value of a car which is 3.5 years old.

(c) Why can the value of a 9 year old car not be reliably estimated from the above data?

Hint:
Draw a line of best fit.

6 There are 190 year 11 students in Heath Hill School.

82 of these students are female.

At the end of year 11 all the students will either stay at school, go to college or start an apprenticeship.

40 females go to college and 8 males start an apprenticeship.
$\frac{3}{5}$ of the 80 students who stay at school are male.

Find the total number of students who go to college.

7 (a) Explain what a simple random sample is.

(b) Anton and Natalia need to each gather a simple random sample from a group of people. Anton writes names on strips of paper of varying sizes. He then mixes them up in a box and chooses 10 strips.
Natalia assigns a number to each person. Each number is placed on a separate ball then the balls are mixed up in a box. She then chooses 10 balls. The balls are all the same size. Are both of these methods likely to produce a simple random sample?
Which is the best method? Give full reasons for your answers.

8

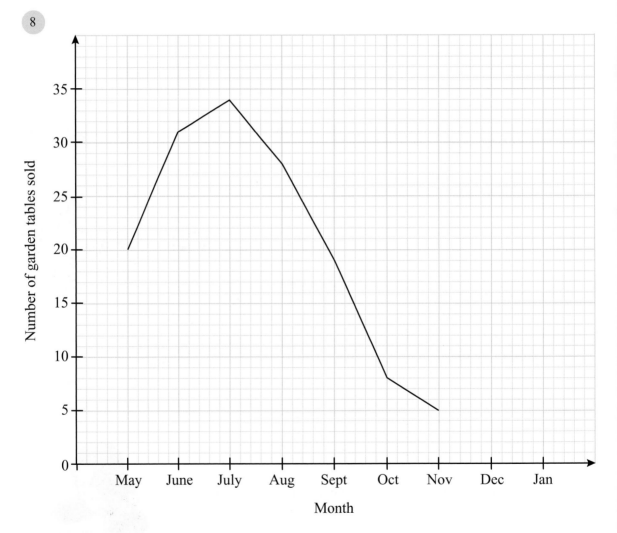

A store sells garden tables. The number sold for some months of the year is shown above. Can the number of garden tables sold in January be reliably predicted using the graph above?
Give reasons for your answer and state any assumptions you have made.

9 Henry records the type of motorbike he sees at a motorbike show.

He sees 90 in total.

The findings are shown in the table below.

Type	Frequency
Kawasaki	16
Yamaha	8
Harley Davidson	14
Ducati	12
Honda	?
Suzuki	20

Represent this information in a suitable diagram or chart.

10 There are 400 people on a beach.
The table below shows some details about these people.

Age	Male	Female
under 21 years	?	?
21–45 years	73	58
over 45 years	69	82

A stratified sample of 40 of these people is taken.

(a) How many females over 45 years old would be in the sample?

(b) There are five males under 21 years old in the sample.
Work out the greatest number of the 400 people who might be females under 21 years old.

11 The students in 4 classes are asked if they prefer swimming or cycling.
The information is used to draw the pie charts shown below:

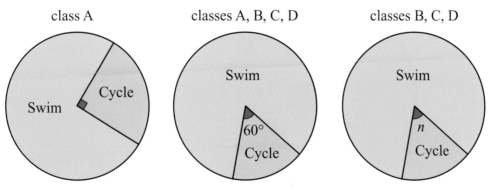

Is $n < 60°$ or $n = 60°$ or $n > 60°$? Explain your answer clearly.

12 160 tourists to London are asked what their favourite sights are. They all choose
Buckingham Palace, Tower Bridge, Big Ben or the Tower of London.

10 of the 85 women choose Tower Bridge.

7 men choose Big Ben. $\frac{3}{4}$ of the 60 people who choose the
Tower of London are men.

70% of the 70 people who choose Buckingham Palace are women.

Find the total number of tourists who choose Big Ben.

13 The pie chart below shows the proportion of the staff in a company who work in sales, the
office, the workshop or as support. It gives the figures for 1st July, 2011 when there were
260 employees in total.

On 1st July, 2010 the number of support staff were exactly half the number of sales staff.

The support staff made up 12% of the total number of employees.

The total number of sales staff increased by 30% from 1st July, 2010 to 1st July, 2011.

Calculate the total number of employees on 1st July, 2010.

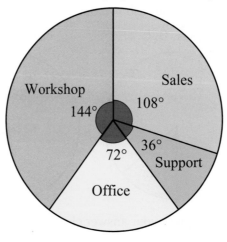

Hint:
Use reverse percentages.

14 The scatter graph below shows the number of drinks Charlie had on certain days and the maximum temperature reached.

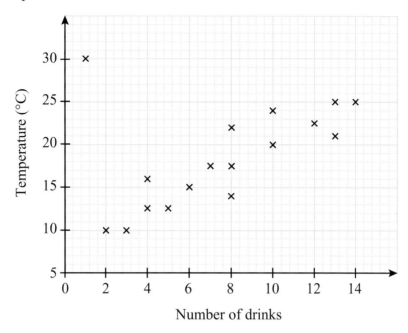

(a) How many drinks would you expect Charlie to have when the maximum temperature is 21°C?

(b) Write down the values of an outlier.

(c) Why can a line of best fit not be used to estimate the number of drinks when the maximum temperature is 0°C?

15

One week on a holiday island there are 1600 people from Great Britain. A holiday rep wishes to ask some people about their level of satisfaction with the holiday. A 5% sample is taken, stratified on the basis of being English, Welsh, Scottish or from Northern Ireland.

If 11 Scots were included in the sample, work out the least number of Scottish people on the holiday island.

1

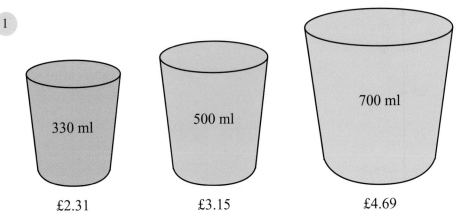

330 ml

500 ml

700 ml

£2.31 £3.15 £4.69

The prices of three different sized cups of cola at a cinema are shown above.

Which cup gives the *best value* for money?

Explain your reasons fully.

2 Some people are asked what their favourite form of transport is.
The information is shown in the table below.

Form of transport	Frequency
Car	8
Boat	20
Plane	14
Bike	16
Train	25
Other	7

Represent this information in a suitable diagram or chart.

3 Alexa has to factorise $4x^3 - 36x$ completely. She writes:
   Answer = $4x(x^2 - 9)$

Alexa is happy with her answer but Harvey is not. Explain clearly why Harvey is not happy.

4 A group of 27 people go to an adventure park.

Their first ride is either on the *Turbo Terror*, the *Curly Whirl* or the *Splashdown*.

Half of the 12 women go on the *Turbo Terror*.

5 men go on the *Splashdown*. 10 people go on the *Curly Whirl*, of whom $\frac{2}{5}$ are women.

How many people in total go on the *Splashdown* first?

5   The total number of goals scored at the end of this season by two football teams, Henton Rovers and Holby City, are in the ratio 2:3 respectively.

This season Henton Rovers scored 20% less goals than last season and Holby City scored $33\frac{1}{3}$% more goals than last season. Holby City scored 54 goals last season.

Which team scored more goals last season and by how many?

> **Hint:**
> Consider the reverse percentage procedure.

6   A shoe shop records the heights and shoe sizes of a number of people.
The information is shown on the scatter graph below.

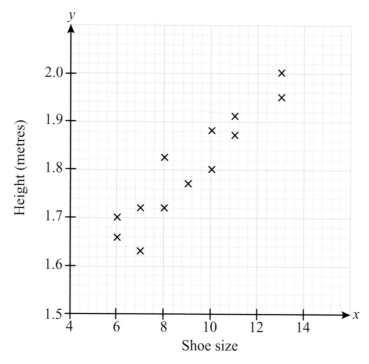

One more person of height 1.82 m has shoe size 11.

(a) Copy the scatter graph and mark on this final person.

(b) Describe the relationship between the shoe sizes and the heights of these people.

(c) Estimate the height of a person with shoe size 12.

(d) Could the graph be extended to estimate the shoe size of a person 1.3 m tall?
Fully justify your answer.

7

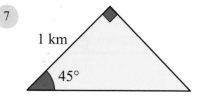

Harley runs twice around the triangular track shown opposite at a constant speed of 4 m/s.

How long does this take Harley to complete (give the answer in minutes to 3 significant figures)?

8   Mr and Mrs Amos want to go to China on holiday. A travel firm gives them the following prices. Each price given is for one adult.

Departure date	7 nights	14 nights	21 nights
2 Sep–16 Sep	£1425	£2065	£2490
17 Sep–1 Oct	£1439	£2081	£2506
2 Oct–23 Oct	£1461	£2110	£2524
24 Oct–14 Nov	£1475	£2126	£2548
15 Nov–5 Dec	£1489	£2153	£2573
6 Dec–20 Dec	£1513	£2198	£2592
21 Dec–4 Jan	£1528	£2215	£2605
5 Jan–26 Jan	£1475	£2153	£2573
27 Jan–17 Feb	£1439	£2081	£2506

The price is reduced for under 16 year-olds as follows:

10% reduction on full price for 7 nights
15% reduction on full price for 14 nights
20% reduction on full price for 21 nights

Mr and Mrs Amos have 3 children aged 9,12 and 17.

The whole family wish to go to China for 14 nights, leaving on 16th October or leaving on 15th December.

How much will they save on the cost of the holiday if they choose to leave on 16th October rather than 15th December?

9

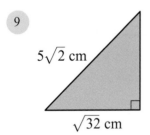

$5\sqrt{2}$ cm

$\sqrt{32}$ cm

Work out the area of this triangle.

10   $\mathscr{E}$ = {integers from 1 to 10 inclusive}
     A = {square numbers}
     B = {orders of rotational symmetry of a trapezium, a square, a regular hexagon and a regular octagon}

(a) Copy and complete the Venn diagram shown opposite.

(b) One number is chosen at random.
Which is greater? $p(A \cap B)'$ or $p(A' \cup B)$
Give full justification for your answer.

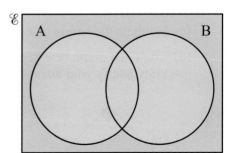

11

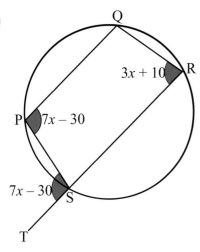

$3x + 10$

$7x - 30$

$7x - 30$

Prove that PQRS is a trapezium.

Hint:
Consider cyclic
quadrilaterals.

12 A window frame is made from a rectangle
with a semi-circle on top.

The diagram shows the straight and curved
pieces of metal which are needed.

Calculate the total length of metal giving
the answer in metres, rounded off to the
nearest cm.

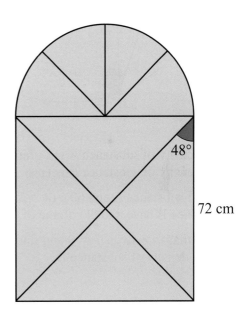

$48°$

72 cm

13

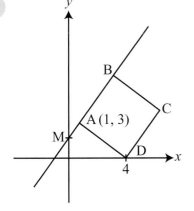

ABCD is a square opposite.

The line through B and A cuts the y-axis at M.

Find the co-ordinates of M.

Hint:
Remember that the product
of the gradients of two
perpendicular lines is -1.

14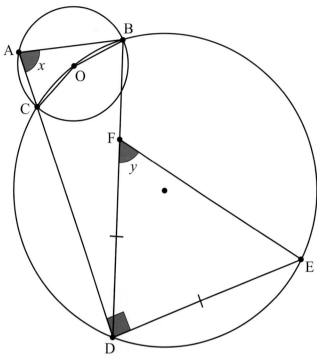

O is the centre of the smaller circle

DF = DE

Angle CDE = 90°

Express y in terms of x.

Explain your answer fully.

15 The density of substance A is x grams/cm³.
The density of substance B is $(x + 3)$ grams/cm³.

21 g of substance A and 60 g of
substance B have a total volume of 9 cm³.

Show that $x^2 - 6x - 7 = 0$ and find the
actual density of substance B.

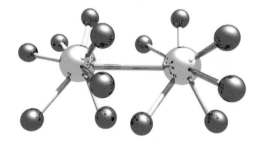

ALGEBRA 3

A

1

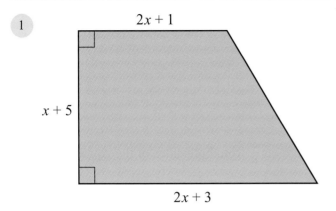

2x + 1

x + 5

2x + 3

The area of this trapezium is 27 cm².

Calculate the value of x correct to two decimal places.

Hint:
Find the area of a trapezium by adding together the two parallel sides and multiplying the answer by half the distance between these two parallel sides.

2 Find the coordinates of the point of intersection of the straight line $3x + 2y = 17$ and the straight line $5x - 3y = 22$.
(Do not draw a graph.)

3 A quadratic sequence has nth term $= n^2 + n + 1$
Prove algebraically whether 157 is a term in the sequence or not.

4 Nathan buys 5 razors and 2 shaving brushes for £9.30

Kevin buys 9 razors and 3 shaving brushes for £15.30

Work out the cost of each razor and each shaving brush.

Hint:
Form simultaneous equations then solve them.

5   Teresa wants to prove that the quadratic equation formula solves the equation
$ax^2 + bx + c = 0$.

She starts with $ax^2 + bx + c = 0$

She divides the equation by a

$$x^2 + \frac{bx}{a} + \frac{c}{a} = 0$$

She now completes the square

$$\left(x + \frac{b}{2a}\right)^2 - \left(\frac{b}{2a}\right)^2 + \frac{c}{a} = 0$$

She squares out the second bracket and subtracts $\frac{c}{a}$ from both sides of the equation.

$$\left(x + \frac{b}{2a}\right)^2 - \frac{b^2}{4a^2} = -\frac{c}{a}$$

She adds $\frac{b^2}{4a^2}$ to both sides of the equation then gets a common denominator for the right hand side of the equation.

$$\left(x + \frac{b}{2a}\right)^2 = \frac{b^2}{4a^2} - \frac{c}{a}$$

$$\left(x + \frac{b}{2a}\right)^2 = \frac{b^2 - 4ac}{4a^2}$$

Complete Teresa's proof to end up with the quadratic equation formula, explaining each step clearly.

6   The distance s travelled by a windsurfer is given by the formula $s = ut + \frac{1}{2}at^2$

where u is the initial velocity of the windsurfer, a is the acceleration of the windsurfer and t is the time taken (in seconds).

Find how long it takes the windsurfer to travel $100\,\text{m}$ if $a = 2$ and $u = 5$.
Give your answer to one decimal place.

7   Tickets for a village pantomime are sold at £9 for an adult and £5 for a child.
On the Friday night ticket sales amount to £715 and the total number of people who attend the pantomime is 95.
How many adults go to the pantomime on the Friday night?

8   The population P of a group of monkeys living on a small island is given by the formula

$$P = m \times 1.2^{nt}$$

where P is rounded off to the nearest whole number and t is measured in years.

(a) Initially (ie. $t = 0$) the population of monkeys is 200. Work out the value of m.

(b) After 1 year the population of monkeys is 288. Work out the value of n.

(c) Find the population of monkeys after 2 years.

(d) During which year does the population of monkeys exceed 1000 for the first time?

9   (a) Draw the graph of $y = 3x^2 - 2x$ for values of x from $x = -3$ to $x = 3$.

(b) Use your graph to find the roots of $3x^2 - 2x = 0$

(c) Use your graph to solve $3x^2 - 2x = 7$

(d) Use your graph to find the roots of $3x^2 - 2x - 4 = 0$

10

$3n$

$3m + 1$

$5n$

$2m - 1$

The dimensions in cm of a rectangular picture are shown opposite.

Find the values of m and n.

11 Work out the length of the line which joins the origin to the turning point of the curve
$y = x^2 + 6x + 5$
(Do not draw the graph for this curve.)

Hint:
Complete the square first.

12

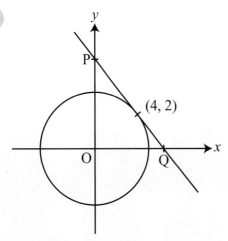

The point (4, 2) lies on the circle $x^2 + y^2 = 20$

The tangent to the circle at (4, 2) meets the y-axis at P and the x-axis at Q.

O is the origin.

Calculate the area of triangle OPQ.

13

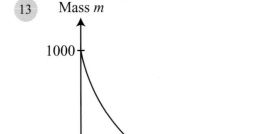

The graph shows how the mass of a radioactive substance decays.

The mass m is measured in grams and the time t is measured in years.

The mass m is given by the formula $m = p(n^{-t})$

Calculate the mass after 6 years.

14 Jodie has an amount (in grams) of substance A and substance B.

When the amount of both is increased by 10 g, the ratio of the amount of substance A to substance B is 2:1.

This ratio changes to 3:2 when the amount of both substances is increased by a further 30 g.

How much of each of substance A and substance B did Jodie have to begin with?

15 The border of a circular piece of parkland can be defined on a map by the equation $x^2 + y^2 = 4$.

Pipes are to be laid in a straight line from points A to B as shown opposite. The path of the pipes can be defined by the equation $2y = x + 2$.

If the radius of the parkland is 2 km, calculate the total length AB of the pipeline within the parkland.

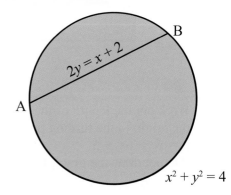

M | MIXED 11

1 Sophie goes to India for three weeks.
She changes £750 into rupees.
The exchange rate is shown below.

£1 = 75 rupees

During her stay in India she spends 50340 rupees.

When Sophie returns home, she gives all the
remaining money to her sister.
Her sister needs £75 to see a music concert.
Is Sophie's remaining money enough for this? Explain your answer fully.

2

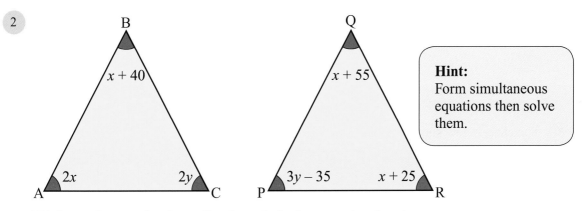

Hint:
Form simultaneous
equations then solve
them.

Work out the actual values of each angle in the two triangles above.

3 (a) Draw x and y axes both labelled from -6 to 6.

(b) Draw a triangle with vertices at $(-4, 5)$, $(-4, 4)$ and $(-2, 4)$.

(c) This triangle is reflected in the line $y = -x$ then the new triangle is reflected in the
line $y = 4$. Write down the co-ordinates of the point (or points) which remain
invariant following these two transformations.

4

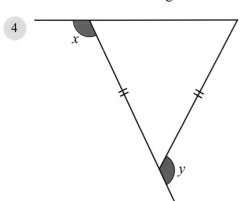

Express y in terms of x.

92

5　On a large farm there are five times as many chicks as cats. The chicks and cats have a total of 98 legs between them.
Work out how many chicks there are.

6　Ashna invests £4000 at 3% compound interest per annum. Julian invests £3500 at 5% compound interest per annum. During which year will Julian first have more money than Ashna? Explain your method fully.

Hint:
Use the multipliers, eg. ×1.02 for 2% compound interest per annum.

7　The chart below shows some train times.

Westbury	1542	1619	1719	1758	1837	1920
Trowbridge	1551	1628	1728	1807	1846	1929
Bath	1601	1638	1738	1817	1856	1939
Bristol	1620	1658	1758	1836	1915	1958

Bristol	2018	2047	2118	2207	2218	2305
Bath	2036	2105	2136	2225	2236	2323
Trowbridge	2046	2115	2146	2235	2246	2333
Westbury	2057	2126	2157	2246	2257	2344

Natalia lives in Westbury.

It takes her 20 minutes to walk from her home to Westbury train station. It takes her 25 minutes to get from Bristol train station to the Hippodrome. She leaves home at the latest possible time so that she can get to the Hippodrome for the start of the Gala Show.

She catches the earliest possible train after the Gala Show back to Westbury and then returns home directly.

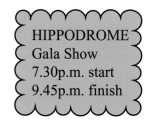

HIPPODROME
Gala Show
7.30p.m. start
9.45p.m. finish

How long is it in total between her leaving home and arriving back home?

8 Chen is making x the subject of the formula given below:

$$\frac{2cx}{b} = \frac{y}{b} + \frac{ax}{b} + d$$

$$2cx = y + ax + bd$$

$$2cx - ax = y + bd$$

$$2x - x = \frac{y + bd}{ac}$$

$$x = \frac{y + bd}{ac}$$

Do you agree with Chen? If not, identify his error clearly then find the correct answer.

9 Rohan makes chairs. The raw materials for each chair cost £18 including VAT.

Rohan is able to claim this VAT back from the Government.

He sells each chair so that he makes an actual profit of £34. In addition to the cost of the raw materials and his profit, the final selling price of each chair must have VAT added to it.

Calculate the selling price of each chair. (Take VAT as 20%)

10

The vertex A lies on the y-axis. AC is horizontal. AB = 6 units.

Triangle ABC is reflected in the line AC so that the image of B has a y-ordinate equal to -5.

Work out the 'exact' co-ordinates of the point B shown opposite.

Hint:
You should not need to use a calculator. 'Exact' means 'leave surds in the answer if necessary'.

11 86 children go on a watersports holiday.
One morning each child will waterski, windsurf or dive.
11 out of the 40 girls go diving.

Half of the 28 children who waterski are boys. 21 boys windsurf.

How many children go diving in total?

12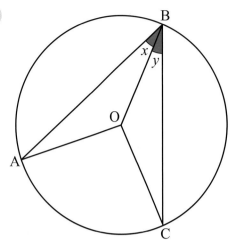

O is the centre of the circle.

Prove that angle AOC $= 2(x + y)$

Which circle property does this prove?

13 A bag contains green and white balls.

If one ball is removed at random, the probability of choosing a green ball is $\frac{1}{4}$.

The original bag of balls has four extra green balls added to it. If one ball is now removed at random, the probability of choosing a green ball is $\frac{2}{5}$.

Work out how many green and white balls were originally in the bag.

14 Two people running in a 400 m race have a combined time of 100 seconds.

(a) If the average speed of the first person is v m/s and the average speed of the second person is $(v + 1)$ m/s, show that

$$v^2 - 7v - 4 = 0$$

(b) Calculate, correct to two decimal places, the average speed of the first person.

15 Find an expression, in terms of x, for the volume of this triangular prism.

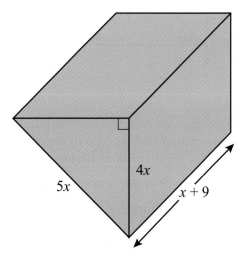

G	**GEOMETRY 3**

1

Field A

Field B

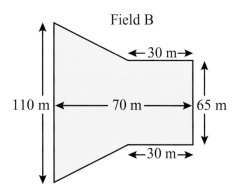

A farmer needs to spray two fields at a cost of £3.87 per 100 m².

Field A is a semi-circle attached to a rectangle. Field B is a trapezium joined to a rectangle.

Which field will be more expensive to spray and by how much?

2

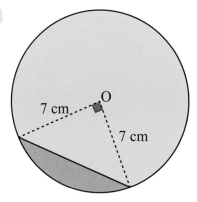

A circular piece of pastry has a small segment cut from it (the grey area shown opposite).

Calculate the percentage of the original piece of pastry which remains, giving your answer to one decimal place.

3 A large house has a drive in front of it as shown opposite.

The diagram shows a smaller semi-circle inside a larger semi-circle.

The drive is to be covered with gravel.

There are two types of gravel available as shown in the table below.

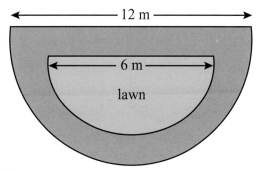

One tonne of gravel A	One tonne of gravel B
Covers 17 m²	Covers 12 m²
Costs £148	Costs £106

The gravel can only be bought in multiples of tonnes.

Which gravel will be cheaper to use and by how much?

4   Tom fills up cylindrical glasses completely from a
    2 litre bottle of drink. Each glass has diameter 5.6 cm
    and height 8.4 cm.
    Given that 1 litre = 1000 cm³, how many glasses can
    Tom fill completely?

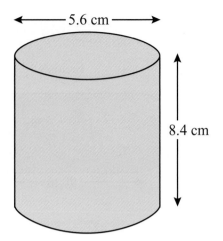

5

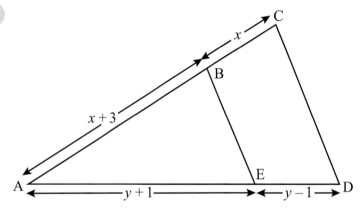

AC = 19 cm
AD = 18 cm

Prove whether BE is parallel
to CD.

Hint:
Are triangles ABE
and ACD similar?

6

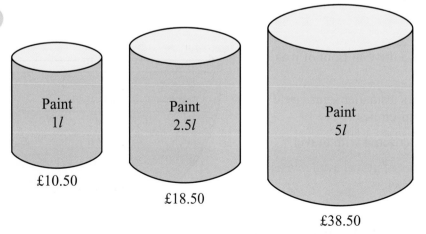

Paint
1*l*

£10.50

Paint
2.5*l*

£18.50

Paint
5*l*

£38.50

Makayla wants to paint 3 walls in a room as shown at the top of
the following page.

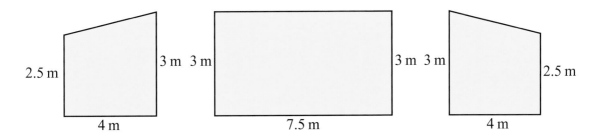

If 1 litre of paint will cover an area of 6 m², which tins of paint must Makayla buy so that she pays the least amount of money? Give full reasons for your answer.

7

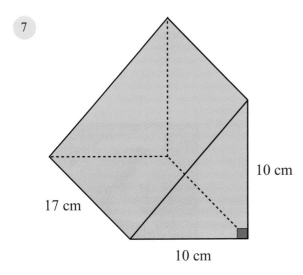

Aaron has a 2 m by 40 cm rectangular sheet of wrapping paper.

He wraps the box shown opposite which is in the shape of a triangular prism.

He uses 40% more wrapping paper than the actual surface area of the box.

Calculate the percentage of the original rectangular sheet of wrapping paper which is used by Aaron to wrap this box.

Give the answer to one decimal place.

8

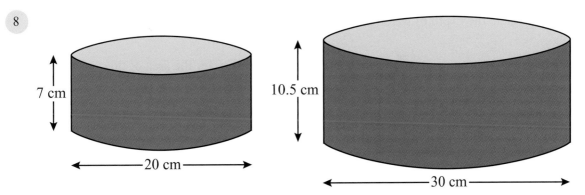

Avery bakes a circular cake of height 7 cm and diameter 20 cm.
She sells this cake for £6.

She now bakes a larger cake of height 10.5 cm and diameter 30 cm.
She wants to sell this cake so that it is the same value per mouthful as the smaller cake.
Work out the price of the larger cake.

9

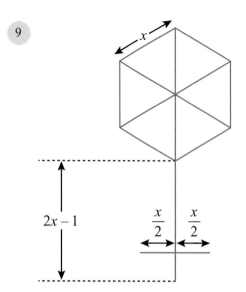

A piece of jewellery is made.

The diagram opposite shows the strips of metal that have been used.
The main shape is a regular hexagon.

Calculate the area of the hexagon, correct to one decimal place, if the total length of metal used is 36.5 cm.

Hint:
Use trigonometry to help find the area of one of the triangles or use the $\frac{1}{2}ab \sin C$ area formula.

10

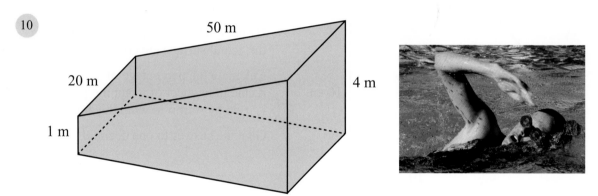

The swimming pool above is filled completely with water. During some very hot weather $30\,m^3$ of the water evaporates so the water level drops.
Calculate the depth of water at the deep end of the pool now.

11

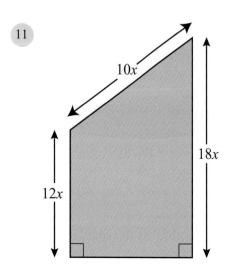

Find an expression for the area of this trapezium in terms of x.

Show all your working out.

Hint:
Hunt around for Pythagoras.

12 Christian uses oil to heat his house.
The oil is stored in a tank which is a regular octagonal prism as shown opposite. The oil costs 62p per litre.

The oil tank is filled up to 55% of its total capacity. Calculate the value of the oil in the tank at this moment.

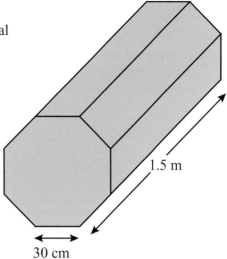

1.5 m

30 cm

13

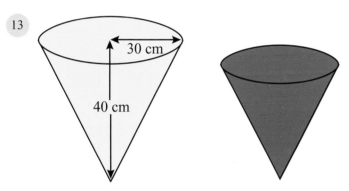

30 cm

40 cm

A cone has radius 30 cm and a perpendicular height of 40 cm.
Another similar cone has a volume which is 48.8% smaller than the volume of the other cone.
Work out the *total* surface area of the smaller cone, leaving your answer in terms of π.

14

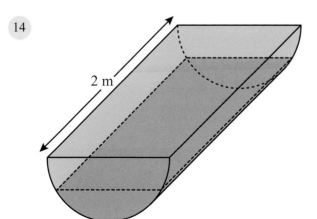

2 m

The front end of this trough is a semicircle with diameter 40 cm.

Calculate the volume of water in the trough when its depth is 4 cm.

15 A frustum is created by cutting a smaller cone away from a larger cone.

Find the volume of the frustum opposite, leaving the answer in the form $k\pi\sqrt{3}$ where the value of k is to be found. *Do not use a calculator.*

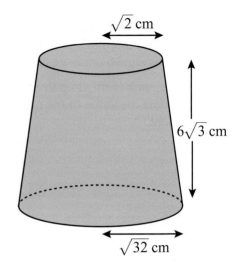

M | MIXED 12

1. Each sweet in a box is either yellow or blue.
   The ratio of yellow to blue is $3\frac{1}{3} : \frac{5}{6}$
   Oscar says that $\frac{4}{5}$ of the sweets are yellow.

   (a) Explain very clearly why Oscar is correct or incorrect.

   (b) There are n yellow sweets in the box. Find an expression, in terms of n, for the total number of sweets in the box.

2. Robert sells caravans for 'Harrison's caravans'.
   He is paid £890 each month plus a bonus if he sells more than 8 caravans as shown below.

Bonus payment: £125 for each extra caravan sold above 8

   Melanie sells caravans for 'Vanpark'.
   She is paid £10 320 per year. She also gets a monthly bonus if she sells more than 9 caravans as shown opposite.

   Bonus:

   £100 for 1 extra sale above 9

   £300 for 2 extra sales above 9

   £550 for 3 extra sales above 9

   £850 for 4 extra sales above 9

Annual personal tax allowance: £9325

Tax rate: 20%

   (a) In April they both sell 12 caravans. Who earns more money that month after income tax has been deducted and by how much?

   (b) In May they both sell 11 caravans. Does the same person still earn more money after income tax has been deducted? Explain your answer fully.

3.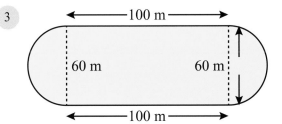

   The diagram above shows a running track made from a rectangle and two semi-circles.
   An athlete runs completely around the track four times.
   Work out the total distance the athlete runs.
   Give the answer to the nearest metre.

4

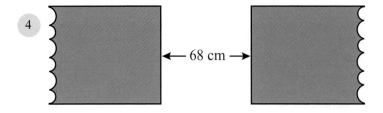

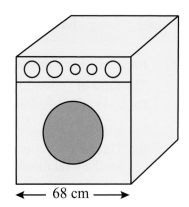

(a) A washing machine has width 68 cm, measured to the nearest cm.

It is to be placed in a gap between two cupboards in a kitchen. The gap has been measured as 68 cm, to the nearest cm.

Explain why the washing machine might not fit into the gap.

(b) A marble worktop is to be made for the kitchen. The worktop dimensions opposite are all measured to the nearest cm.

What is the maximum possible area of this worktop surface?

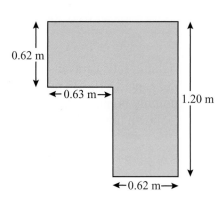

5 Payton drives from Glastonbury to Moreton-in-Marsh and back again. The reading on her speedometer before and after is shown below.

Her car does 32 miles on one gallon of petrol.

The cost of petrol is shown below.

£1.55 per litre

How much does it cost Payton to drive from Glastonbury to Moreton-in-Marsh and back again.
Give your answer to the nearest penny. (Assume 1 gallon = 4.5 litres)

6 Calculate the area of this parallelogram.

Give the answer to one decimal place.

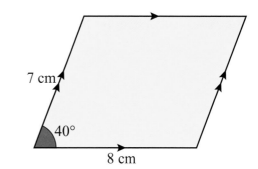

7 cm

40°

8 cm

> **Hint:**
> Area of parallelogram
> = base × perpendicular height
> Look for trigonometry.

7 The cardboard box opposite
measures 100 cm × 75 cm × 55 cm.

Julian has 80 packets with the
dimensions 25 cm × 25 cm × 10 cm.

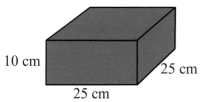

10 cm

25 cm

25 cm

Julian puts as many packets as possible
into the cardboard box and seals it.

How many packets are left over?

8

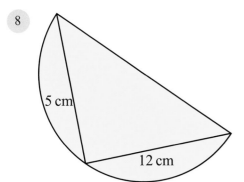

5 cm

12 cm

Calculate the perimeter of this semi-circle.

Give your answer to one decimal place.

9

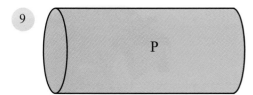

P

Q

surface area = 1.44×10^8 cm²
volume = 1.728×10^{12} cm³

surface area = 1.764×10^9 cm²
volume = 7.4088×10^{13} cm³

Show clearly whether cylinders P and Q are similar or not. Explain your answer fully.

10 Use algebra to prove that the square of any odd number is always an odd number.

Hint:
Let any odd number be $2n + 1$

11

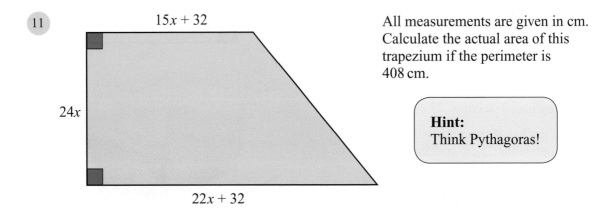

All measurements are given in cm. Calculate the actual area of this trapezium if the perimeter is 408 cm.

Hint:
Think Pythagoras!

12 (a) Draw the graph of $y = x^3 - 2x^2 - x + 2$ for values of x from $x = -2$ to $x = 3$.

(b) Explain how to use your graph to solve $x^3 - 2x^2 - x + 2 = 0$

(c) Use your graph to find the roots of $x^3 - 2x^2 - x + 2 = 4$

(d) Explain how to use your graph to find the roots of $x^3 - 2x^2 - x + 4 = 0$

13

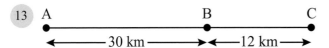

A car travels from A to B at a constant speed of x km/h and from B to C at a constant speed of $(x - 6)$ km/h.

Find an algebraic expression, in terms of x, for the car's average speed when travelling from A to C. Give the answer as a simplified fraction.

14 Terry has some car repairs done at his local garage.

He is told how much the bill is and has just enough money to cover it.

Unfortunately the garage quote did not include the VAT.

When Terry gets the actual bill including VAT, it amounts to £270.
Assume VAT is 20%.

Calculate how much more money Terry needs to cover this bill than he first thought.

15

$x - 5$

The width of the rectangle opposite is $(x - 5)$ cm as shown. Its length is 1 cm greater than its width.

The perimeter of the rectangle is greater than 2 cm. Its area has a maximum possible value of 6 cm².

Form and solve the inequalities to find the range of values between which x must lie.

STATISTICS 3

1. Ten people threw a dice. Their scores are shown in the bar chart below.

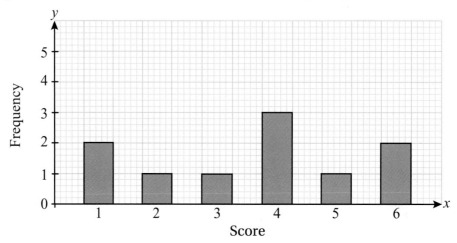

Calculate the mean score and the median score.

2. Brooke went ice skating in two different cities. In each ice skating centre she randomly asked 25 people for their ages. These ages are shown in the back-to-back stem and leaf diagram below.

Birmingham		Bristol
9 9 9 6	0	7 8 8
6 6 5 4 4 3 2 2	1	2 5 5 6 6 7 9
8 8 7 6 4 4 4 3 3	2	1 2 2 4 7
4 3 3 2	3	2 4 5 5 9
	4	3 6 6 7
	5	2

| Key 3\|2 means 23 years old | | Key 2\|4 means 24 years old |

(a) What was the probability that a person chosen in Bristol would be more than 40 years old?

(b) There were a total of 100 people in the ice skating centre at Bristol. How many of these people were likely to have been more than 40 years old?

> **Hint:**
> 'Compare sets of data' particularly means 'compare *averages* and compare *spread* (eg. range or interquartile range)'.

(c) Compare the ages of the people in Birmingham with the ages of the people in Bristol.

3   8, *m* and *n* are different positive integers, each written on a separate card.

| 8 | | *m* | | *n* |

The mean average of these three numbers is 6.
There are several different possible pairs of values for *m* and *n*.
How many pairs of values are there?

4   Two teams, the Warriors and the Sabres, compete
against each other in jetbike racing. Each team
has five members.
Each member completes four circuits.
The mean average time for all the circuits is calculated.
The team with the lowest time wins the competition.

The circuit times for the Warriors are shown in the
table below.

Time (T) in minutes	Frequency
$6 < T \leqslant 6.5$	3
$6.5 < T \leqslant 7$	5
$7 < T \leqslant 7.5$	6
$7.5 < T \leqslant 8$	4
$8 < T \leqslant 8.5$	2

The mean average time for the Sabres is
7 minutes 8.2 seconds.

Using an estimate for the mean average
time for the Warriors, which team wins the
competition? Write down the difference in the
mean average times.

> **Hint:**
> Use mid-values for each interval when
> estimating the mean average.

5   27 students from a Music College go for a drink.
Their main instruments are either piano, violin or cello.
9 of the 15 women play the violin. $\frac{2}{3}$ of the six piano
players are men. 6 men play the cello.
How many students in total play the violin?

6   The stem and leaf diagram below shows the number of goals scored by football teams in the Premiership during one season.

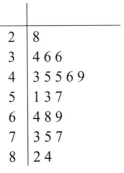

2	8
3	4 6 6
4	3 5 5 6 9
5	1 3 7
6	4 8 9
7	3 5 7
8	2 4

Key 6|8 means 68 goals

The box plot opposite shows the number of goals scored by football teams in the Championship during the same season.

Compare fully the number of goals scored by the Premiership teams to the number of goals scored by the Championship teams.

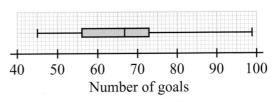

Number of goals

7   Some students take a Science test. Their marks are shown in the table below.

Mark, m (%)	$0 < m \leqslant 20$	$20 < m \leqslant 40$	$40 < m \leqslant 60$	$60 < m \leqslant 80$	$80 < m \leqslant 100$
Frequency	8	26	12	22	10

Gina draws a cumulative frequency graph below to display this information.

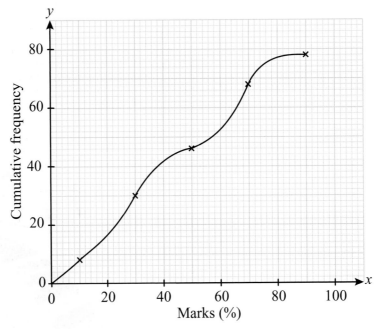

(a) Gina has made some mistakes when drawing this graph. Identify these mistakes.

(b) Explain exactly how the interquartile range would be found from this graph.

8   Classes 11P and 11Q both take the same Maths test. The box plots below show information about the test results for each class.

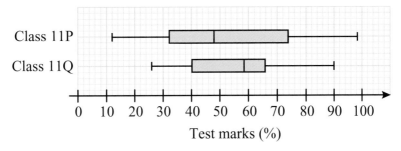

Class 11P

Class 11Q

0   10   20   30   40   50   60   70   80   90   100

Test marks (%)

(a) There are 28 pupils in class 11P. How many pupils in class 11P score more than 74% in the test?

(b) Compare fully the test marks for class 11P to the test marks for class 11Q.

9   The weights of many of the tigers in captivity are recorded. The information is shown in the histogram below. 28 tigers weigh 210 kg to 230 kg.

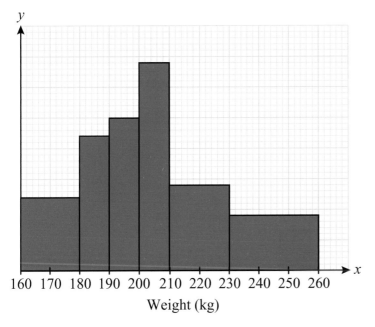

y

160   170   180   190   200   210   220   230   240   250   260 x

Weight (kg)

Calculate the probability that one of these tigers chosen at random would weigh more than 250 kg.

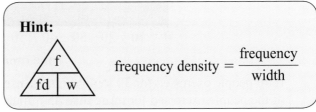

Hint:

f

fd w

$$\text{frequency density} = \frac{\text{frequency}}{\text{width}}$$

10 Two market gardeners each sample some of their tomatoes by examining the weights of the tomatoes. The information is shown in the tables below.

Gardener 1	
Weight w (grams)	Frequency
$60 < w \leqslant 80$	5
$80 < w \leqslant 100$	9
$100 < w \leqslant 120$	14
$120 < w \leqslant 140$	10
$140 < w \leqslant 160$	25
$160 < w \leqslant 180$	16
$180 < w \leqslant 200$	12
$200 < w \leqslant 220$	8
$220 < w \leqslant 240$	1

Gardener 2	
Weight w (grams)	Frequency
$60 < w \leqslant 80$	8
$80 < w \leqslant 100$	10
$100 < w \leqslant 120$	15
$120 < w \leqslant 140$	17
$140 < w \leqslant 160$	30
$160 < w \leqslant 180$	30
$180 < w \leqslant 200$	6
$200 < w \leqslant 220$	4

(a) Draw cumulative frequency graphs for the weights of the tomatoes for each gardener.

(b) Compare fully the weights of the tomatoes for gardener 1 with the weights of the tomatoes for gardener 2.

11 The histogram below shows how much time a group of people spent exercising in the gym on one Wednesday.

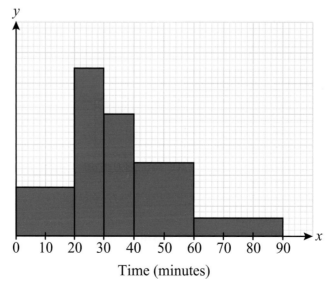

Time (minutes)

If 40 people exercised for 30 to 40 minutes, use the histogram to estimate what proportion of the people exercised for more than 45 minutes.

12 Some people were asked how many portions of fruit and vegetables they eat each day.
$4x$ men were asked and they gave a mean number of portions equal to 2.5
$3y$ children were asked and they gave a mean number of portions equal to 3.
$2x$ women were asked and they gave a mean number of portions equal to 4.
Work out the mean number of portions for all the people combined.

13 Several people are asked to count the number of birds they see
in their garden each day.

The results are shown in the table below.

Number of birds	1–5	6–10	11–15	16–20	21–25	26–30
Number of people	n	7	16	$7n$	15	10

Work out exactly how many people counted 16–20 birds if the
mean average number of birds counted above was 17.5625

14 The cumulative frequency graph below shows information about the salaries of the 40
people who work for Hensons Engineering Firm.

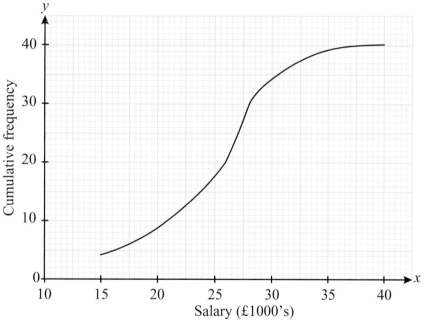

The lowest actual salary is £14 000 and the highest actual salary is £39 000.

(a) '25% of the people earn £21 000 or less.'
    Is this statement correct?
    Explain your answer fully.

(b) The box plot shows information
    about the salaries of people who
    work for the Tadweld Company.

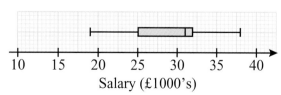

Compare fully the salaries for the people in Hensons Engineering Firm with the salaries of
the people who work for the Tadweld Company.

15 The heights of 28 people are measured.
The information is shown in the histogram below.

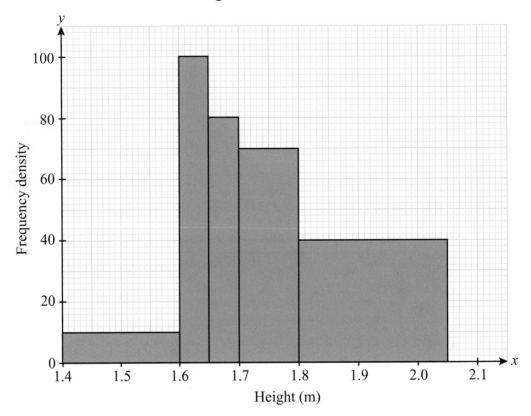

Use the histogram to estimate the mean height (to 2 decimal places).

MIXED 13

1

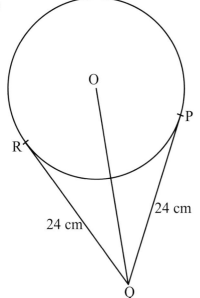

O is the centre of the circle.

QP and QR are tangents to the circle.

OQ = 26 cm

PQ = QR = 24 cm

Calculate the area of the circle, giving your answer to one decimal place.

2

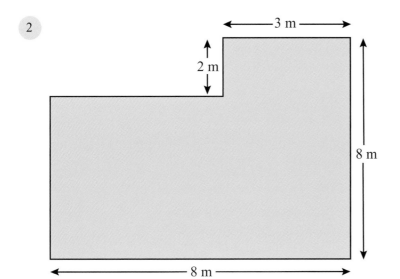

Ayden wants to carpet the room shown above.

Any carpet he buys will be 6 m wide.

He only wants one line where two pieces of carpet join together.

The carpet costs £25 per square metre.

What is the least amount Ayden will have to spend to carpet the entire room?
Explain your working out fully.

3 Find the value of the length x if the triangle and the rectangle both have the same area.

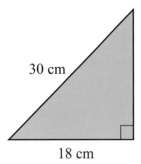
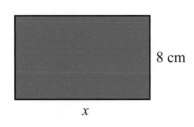

4 A shop sells shirts of various colours. If a shirt is chosen at random, the probability of choosing a short sleeved shirt is 0.45 and the probability of choosing a blue shirt is 0.2 Henry says that the probability of choosing a short sleeved shirt *or* a blue shirt is 0.65 Explain clearly why Henry is not correct.

5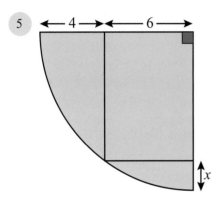

The diagram opposite shows a rectangle within a quarter circle. The lengths are given in cm.

Work out the value of x.

6 Candice is researching how often people take the bus. She asks 40 people in a city and 40 people in a village how often they took a bus in the last week.

The table below shows the results for the city.

City	
Number of bus trips (n)	Frequency
$0 \leqslant n \leqslant 2$	14
$3 \leqslant n \leqslant 5$	6
$6 \leqslant n \leqslant 8$	3
$9 \leqslant n \leqslant 11$	15
$12 \leqslant n \leqslant 15$	2

The maximum number of bus trips taken by one person is 15 and the minimum number is 0.

The village mean and range is shown below.

Village
Mean = 1.3 bus trips
Range = 10 bus trips

Compare fully the number of bus trips taken by people in the city with the number of bus trips taken by people in the village.

7 Calculate the value of *x* opposite.
Show your working out fully.
Give your final answer to one
decimal place.

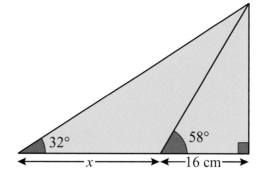

8 Mr Moore is 63 years old and wants to wallpaper two walls in his living room.
The size of the rectangular walls is shown below.

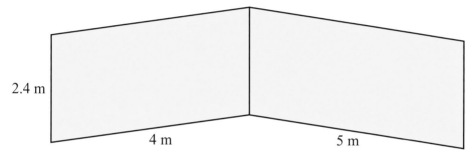

Each roll of wallpaper measures 10 m by 55 cm.

Mr Moore is advised to leave at least 1 cm extra wallpaper whenever he reaches the top or
bottom of the wall.

He also needs tins of wallpaper paste. Each tin covers 8 m². In addition to the wallpaper
and paste, Mr Moore decides that he must buy wallpaper scissors and a wallpaper brush.

The cost of each item in his local store is
shown opposite.

The store offers over 60 year-olds a 10%
discount on Wednesdays. Calculate the
least amount of money that Mr Moore will
have to spend if he buys the items on a
Wednesday morning.

Item	Cost
One roll of wallpaper	£17.49
One tin of paste	£5.99
Scissors	£5.69
Brush	£4.99

9 Dan cycles directly from A to B then B to C then C to D

where $\overrightarrow{AB} = \begin{pmatrix} 7 \\ 21 \end{pmatrix}$, $\overrightarrow{BC} = \begin{pmatrix} 4 \\ -3 \end{pmatrix}$ and $\overrightarrow{CD} = \begin{pmatrix} 3 \\ 30 \end{pmatrix}$.

The numbers are given in km.
If Dan had been able to cycle directly from A to D,
how much less distance would he have cycled?
Give your answer to one decimal place.

Hint:
Draw a diagram first showing
Dan's journey. Use the vectors to
examine right-angled triangles.

10 4, 13, 26, 43, … form a quadratic sequence.
Prove that 859 is in this sequence.

Hint:
Firstly find the nth term formula for this sequence.

11 The cumulative frequency graph below shows information about how many weekly hours of work are carried out by 60 people who work for the Harris Furniture Firm.

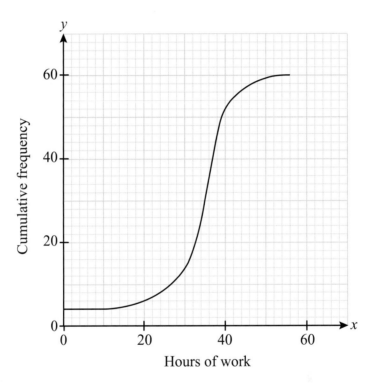

Hours of work

(a) What percentage of the people work for more than 40 hours?

(b) The stem and leaf diagram opposite shows how many weekly hours of work are carried out by the 23 people who work for Mason's Sofa Company.

Compare fully the weekly hours worked by people at the Harris Furniture Firm with the weekly hours worked by people at Mason's Sofa Company.

```
0 | 8
1 | 5  5
2 | 2  7  9  9
3 | 4  6  8  8
4 | 2  2  3  3  3  5  5  8
5 | 1  7
6 | 0  2
```

Key 3|6 means
36 hours of work

12 (a) Explain why an odd number can be written as $2n + 1$.

(b) The next odd number is $2n + 3$. Prove that the sum of any four consecutive odd numbers is always divisible by 8.

Hint:
An expression written in the form 3(…) means it is divisible by 3.

13 Mr and Mrs Benson are looking to stay at the Mendip Hotel or the Magenta Hotel. The prices are shown below.

	Mendip Hotel		Magenta Hotel	
	B&B price per person		B&B price per person	
arrival date	3 nights	each extra night	2 nights	each extra night
7 Feb–14 Apr	£105	£27	£95	£32
15 Apr–10 Jun	£110	£28	£88	£30
11 Jun–30 Aug	£133	£32	£104	£37
31 Aug–30 Oct	£108	£29	£99	£35
31 Oct–4 Jan	£128	£31	£103	£39
5 Jan–6 Feb	£102	£27	£93	£32

Mendip Hotel dinner price per person	
7 Feb–15 Jul	£28.50
16 Jul–6 Feb	£25.50

Magenta Hotel dinner price per person	
7 Feb–30 Jun	£24.75
1 Jul–1 Sep	£29.25
2 Sep–6 Feb	£26.25

If Mr and Mrs Benson book through a holiday agency they will receive a 15% discount on the Mendip Hotel prices and an 18% discount on the Magenta Hotel prices.

Mr and Mrs Benson wish to have a holiday for 4 nights in May. They will eat dinner in the hotel for two of the four nights.

Which hotel will be cheaper and by how much, assuming that they book through the holiday agency?

14 The diagram shows a prism with a cylinder bored through it.

All measurements are in cm.

The volume of the remaining solid is V cm³.

The diameter of the base of the cylinder is x cm.

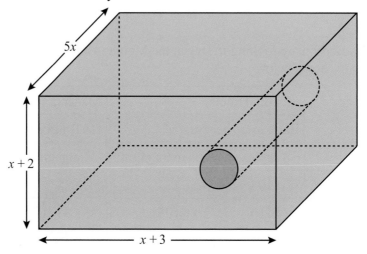

(a) Express V in terms of x.

(b) The density of this prism is $2x$ grams/cm³. Find a formula for the mass m of the remaining solid, in terms of x.

15 In the 2008 Olympics, a country wins m gold medals and n silver medals.

In the 2012 Olympics, the country won 4 more gold medals than in 2008 and 6 more silver.

The ratio of gold to silver was 4:3

In the following 2016 Olympics, the country won the same number of gold medals as in 2012 but 5 less silver than in 2012.

The ratio of gold to silver was 8:5

Work out the ratio of gold to silver medals in 2008 (give the answer in its lowest terms).

G GEOMETRY 4

1 North

Malby

40°

Henton

The bearing of Malby from Henton is 040°.

Explain clearly why the bearing of Henton from Malby is 220°.

2 A vintage car is filled with one gallon of petrol.

The car will travel 6 miles on each litre of petrol.

The car travels 9 miles due south from a petrol pump then 7 miles due west.

Will it have enough petrol to travel directly back to the petrol pump? You must explain your reasons fully.

1 gallon = 4.5 litres

3 In the triangles opposite,
AE = 10 cm, AC = 15 cm and CD = 7 cm
AB is parallel to CD.

(a) Prove that triangles ABC and CDE are similar.

(b) Work out the area of triangle ABC.

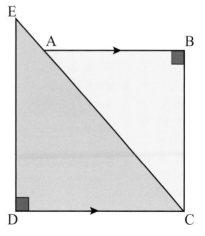

4 Some walkers leave their camp and walk due south for 6 miles. They then walk on a bearing of 325° until they are exactly due west of the camp.

Calculate how far they are from the camp at this point.

Hint:
Use trigonometry.

5 Cotton stands 65 m horizontally from the base of a wind turbine. He uses a theodolite to measure the angle of elevation of the top of the wind turbine. This angle of elevation is 18.7°.

Calculate the height of the top of the wind turbine.

6

Evie has used compasses and ruler only to construct the perpendicular bisector of line PQ.

Explain fully why the perpendicular bisector construction method works.

Hint:
Consider the properties of a rhombus.

7

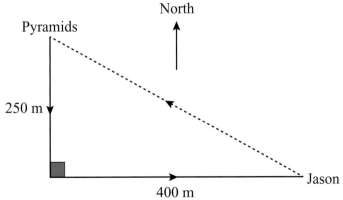

Jason walks 250 m south from some pyramids then 400 m east.

On what bearing must he now walk if he wants to return directly to the pyramids?

8 A pencil case is in the shape of a cuboid
as shown below.

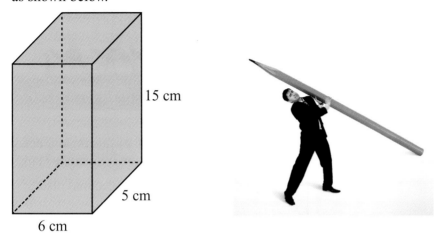

15 cm

5 cm

6 cm

Can a 16.5 cm long pencil fit into the pencil case?
Explain your answer fully.

9 An L-shaped prism is shown below. The three-dimensional co-ordinates of the visible
vertices are indicated. The units are in cm.

Work out the total surface area of the prism.

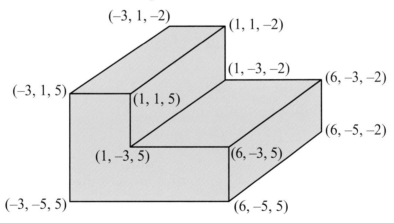

(−3, 1, −2) (1, 1, −2)

(1, −3, −2) (6, −3, −2)

(−3, 1, 5) (1, 1, 5)

(6, −5, −2)

(1, −3, 5) (6, −3, 5)

(−3, −5, 5) (6, −5, 5)

10 Calculate the value of x, showing all
your working out fully.

Give the answer to one decimal place.

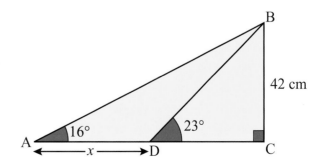

B

42 cm

A 16° 23°

x D C

122

11 Some travellers in the desert leave an oasis on a
    bearing of 073°.

    After 16 km they change direction and travel on
    a bearing of 125°.
    They walk for 9 km then stop.

    On what bearing are they now from the oasis and
    how far are they from the oasis?

12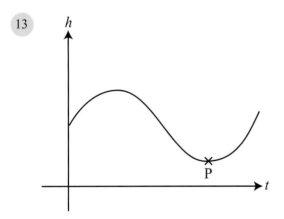

Calculate the height h of this regular octagon if
each side of the octagon has length 3 cm.

Give your answer to two decimal places.

13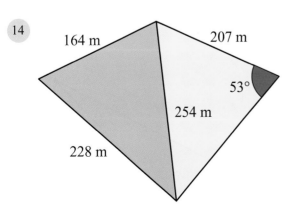

The graph shows the equation

$$h = 4 + 2\sin t$$

Explain why it is known that the minimum
point P has co-ordinates (270, 2).

14

The table below shows how much profit a
farmer can expect from planting barley and
wheat.

| Wheat £800 per hectare |
| Barley £1230 per hectare |

The farmer must plant one of the triangular
fields shown opposite with wheat and one
with barley. Calculate the maximum profit the
farmer can expect. [1 hectare = 10 000 m².]

15 The curve $y = x^2$ is transformed into the curve shown opposite.

Find the equation of the curve shown opposite.

Hint:
The answer will be of the form $y = a(x \pm b)^2$ where a and b are integers to be found.

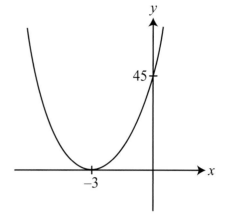

1. Edward plans to wallpaper two complete walls in his living room.

   Each wall is 2.5 m high and a plan of the living room is shown opposite.

   A wallpaper roll is 8 m long and 80 cm wide.

   Each roll of wallpaper costs £18.50

   How many rolls of wallpaper will Edward need and what will be the total cost?

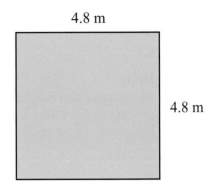

4.8 m

4.8 m

2.

ABCDEFGH is a regular octagon.

AHQR is a rectangle.

GH = GP

HQ = HP

Angle GPH = x

Express angle PQH in terms of x.

3 The ages of footballers in two team squads are shown below.

Forest United	
Age	Frequency
19	2
20	4
21	2
22	7
23	1
24	4

Castle Rangers

1 | 7 8

2 | 2 2 2 3 3 4 4 5 6 6 7 7 7 8 8 8 9 9 9 9

3 | 0 1 1

Key 2|4 means 24

By calculating the mean and range for each team, compare the ages of the footballers in Forest United with those in Castle Rangers.

4
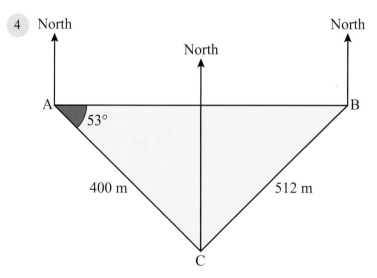

Three balloons are in the positions shown above.
Calculate the bearing of balloon C from balloon B.
Give your answer to one decimal place.

Hint:
A bearing is measured clockwise from the North line.

5　Kate goes for a run.
She runs the first 600 m at
a steady speed of 4 m/s.
The second part of her run
is shown on the velocity/time
graph opposite. She then
finishes by running 800 m
at a steady speed of 9 km/h.

Work out how far Kate
runs in total and how long
it takes her.

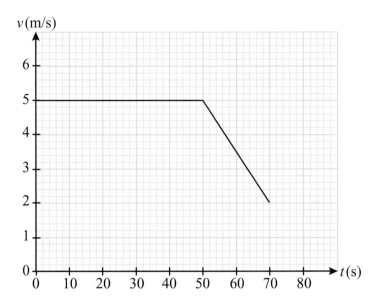

6　Most people have to pay a tax called National Insurance.
Some workers have to pay 11% National Insurance
on all their earnings above £95 a week.

(a) During an average week Jason earns £8.30 an hour
and works for a total of 38 hours.
Assuming 52 weeks in a year, how much
National Insurance will Jason pay each month?

(b) Kaylee earns £9.25 an hour.
During an average week she works for 40 hours
plus 4 hours overtime.
She is paid time and a half for any overtime work.
Assuming 52 weeks in a year, how much National
Insurance will Kaylee pay each month?

7　ABCD is a parallelogram.

BC = 17 cm

BD = 30 cm

AC = 22 cm

(a) Calculate the value of angle CBD.

(b) Calculate the area of ABCD.
Give each answer to one decimal place.

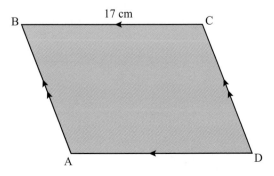

8 Write down any four consecutive numbers.
Multiply together the two outer numbers then multiply together the two inner numbers.
Now subtract the smaller answer from the larger one.
The answer should be 2.

(a) Prove algebraically that this happens with any four consecutive numbers.

(b) Do the same with four consecutive odd numbers.
What result is always obtained and prove it algebraically.

> **Hint:**
> Two consecutive numbers can be written as n and $(n + 1)$.
> Two consecutive odd numbers can be written as $(2n + 1)$ and $(2n + 3)$.

9 Carlos wants to build a wall. He needs to buy 480 bricks.
He finds three deals on the internet.

Deal 1
£26 for a box of 32 bricks

Deal 2
£17 for a box of 16 bricks
Buy 5 boxes and get one extra box free

Deal 3
£70 for a box of 80 bricks
10% discount on 5 or more boxes

Which deal will cost Carlos the least money?
Explain your reasons fully.

10 A farmer uses the field below for his herd of cows.

If he allows 50 m² for each cow, calculate the maximum number of cows he can have in the field at any one time.

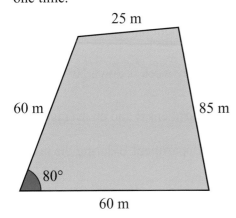

128

11 The ratio $a:b = \sqrt[3]{2}:8$ and the ratio $b:c = 32:\sqrt{2}$
Find the ratio $a:c$ leaving the answer in the form $2^k:1$ where k is to be found.

12

Average number of phone calls made per day		
Department	Regular staff	Temporary staff
A	11	7
B	12	7
C	10	8

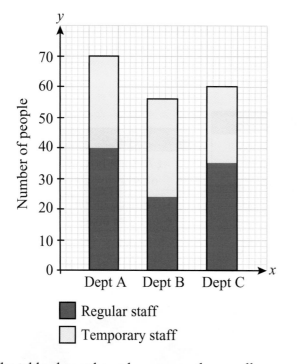

■ Regular staff
□ Temporary staff

The table above shows how many phone calls are made each day by sales staff in three departments in a firm.

On average every 10 calls produces £40 worth of sales.

The graph shows how many staff there are in each department on each of the seven days of the week.

The total amount of Department B sales for this seven day week is down 20% on the Department B sales for the previous week.

In the previous week there were 36 regular staff in Department B and on average every 10 calls produced £25 worth of sales.
How many temporary staff were working each day in Department B during the previous week?

13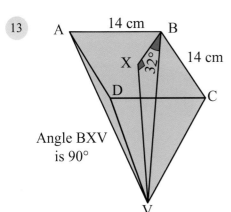

Angle BXV is 90°

The square-based pyramid shown has perpendicular height VX.

The point X is in the middle of square base ABCD.

The cone has perpendicular height 19 cm.

Which container has the greater volume and by how much?

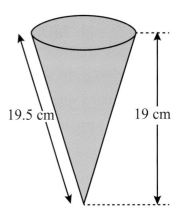

14 Murray throws a dice 40 times. His scores are shown in the frequency table below.

Score	Frequency
1	10
2	8
3	6
4	7
5	7
6	2

Linda throws a dice a number of times. Her scores are shown in the frequency table below.

Score	Frequency
1	11
2	18
3	14
4	★
5	12
6	10

Linda has an ink splodge covering the frequency for the score 4.
It is known that her mean score is 0.345 higher than Murray's mean score.
Work out how many times Linda threw the score 4.

15 There are two tangents to the circle $x^2 + y^2 = 5$ at the points $(-1, 2)$ and $(-1, -2)$. Work out the co-ordinates of the point where these two tangents intersect each other.

Hint:
Sketch a diagram and consider gradients to find the equations of each tangent.

| M | **MIXED 15** |

1 A glass in the shape of a cylinder has radius 3.5 cm.

It is filled with lemonade to a height of 6 cm.

Carly's parents fill 50 glasses in this way for a party.

They buy the lemonade in one litre bottles.

How many bottles of lemonade do they need?

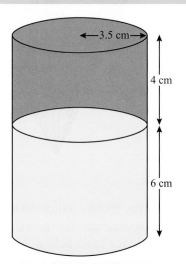

2 Cooper has two dogs, one weighing
19.4 kg and the other weighing 9.8 kg.

The amount of dog food to be eaten
each day is shown below.

Weight of dog (kg)	Amount of food
Up to 11	$\frac{1}{4}$ can
11 to 20	$\frac{1}{3}$ can
20 to 30	$\frac{1}{2}$ can

Cooper buys the dog food from his local store. The prices are shown in the table below.

1 can for 60p

3 cans for £1.70

6 cans for £3.20

Cooper wants to buy enough cans of dog food for all the
month of March to feed both his dogs.

What is the least amount of money he must spend?

Explain your answer fully.

3 There were 1400 students attending a school last year. 20% of these students were in the
Sixth Form. This year the school population has increased by 10%. The number of students
in the Sixth Form is now 25% of the whole school population. By what percentage has the
number of students in the Sixth Form increased compared to last year? Give the answer to
one decimal place.

4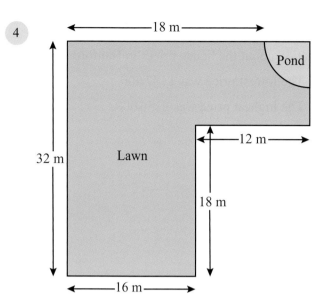

Maria wants to spread fertiliser over her lawn.

Her garden has a pond in the shape of quarter of a circle.

Each packet of fertiliser covers 42 m² of grass and costs £4.60.

How much will it cost Maria to cover all her lawn if the fertiliser packets are sold at a 25% discount?

5 In the Venn diagram opposite:

$n(\mathscr{E}) = 80$

$p(A \cap B) = 0.2$

$p(B') = 0.45$

$n((A \cup B)') = 25$

Work out $n(A)$.

Give full reasons for your answer.

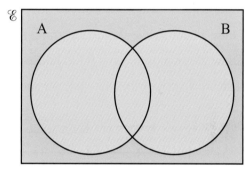

6 A mountaineer travels 1600 m on a bearing of 115°.
His partner travels 900 m from the same starting point on a bearing of 125° and then stops.

The mountaineer now wishes to walk directly to his partner.
On what bearing must he travel?
Give the answer to the nearest whole number.

Hint:
Sketch a diagram then consider sine and cosine rules.

7 Ryan walks *n* km in 10 hours.

Explain fully why his speed can be written as $\dfrac{n}{36}$ m/s.

8   Riya investigates house prices in two areas, one in Hanford and the other in Matwick.

The frequency table below gives information about the house prices in Hanford.

House price (p) ($£1000$'s)	Frequency
$140 < p \leqslant 150$	4
$150 < p \leqslant 160$	2
$160 < p \leqslant 170$	4
$170 < p \leqslant 180$	10
$180 < p \leqslant 190$	14
$190 < p \leqslant 200$	34
$200 < p \leqslant 210$	6
$210 < p \leqslant 230$	4
$230 < p \leqslant 260$	2

The lowest price was £147 000.

The highest price was £256 000.

(a) Draw a cumulative frequency graph to show these house prices.

(b) Draw a box plot to show these house prices.

(c) The house prices for Matwick are shown in the box plot below.

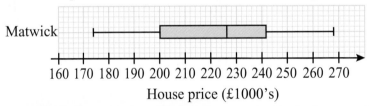

Matwick

160 170 180 190 200 210 220 230 240 250 260 270

House price (£1000's)

Compare fully the house prices in Hanford with the house prices in Matwick.

9   The total area of the rectangle and square opposite is $4 \, \text{cm}^2$.

Joel works out the value of x as shown below:

$x(5x - 5) + x^2 = 4$

$5x^2 - 5x + x^2 = 4$

$6x^2 - 5x - 4 = 0$

$(6x + 2)(x - 2) = 0$

$6x + 2 = 0$ or $x - 2 = 0$

$6x = -2$ or $x = 2$

$x = -\frac{1}{3}$

so $x = 2$ cm (x is a length so cannot be negative)

Is Joel correct? If not, identify his error and work out the true value of x.

$5x - 5$

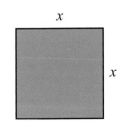

x

x

10

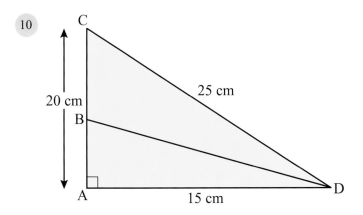

AB:BC = 2:3

Calculate the value of angle BDC.

Give the answer to one decimal place.

11

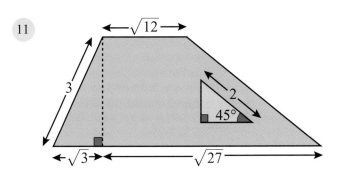

The diagram opposite shows a trapezium with a triangle cut out of it. The units are in cm.
Show that the pink area is $(9\sqrt{2} - 1)$ cm² without using a calculator.

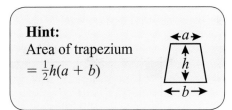

Hint:
Area of trapezium
$= \frac{1}{2}h(a + b)$

12

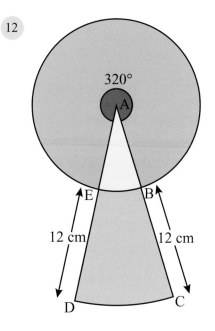

DC is an arc with centre of its circle at A.

The green area is a sector of a circle with centre A.

Calculate the exact value of the blue area if the green sector has an area equal to 72π cm².

Leave the answer in terms of π.

134

13 Tax allowance £8465

The amount of income tax payable for one year is calculated using the tax rates shown opposite.

20% tax payable on first £34 035 of taxable income

40% tax payable on any taxable income above £34 035

Jaxon earns £4167 each month.
Amber earns £1082 each week.
How much more tax does Amber pay for the whole year than Jaxon?
Assume 1 year = 52 weeks.

14 A line with gradient 3 passes through the vertex of the curve $y = x^2 - 4x + 7$

At what co-ordinates does the line meet the curve again?

Hint:

Find the co-ordinates of the vertex by completing the square.

15

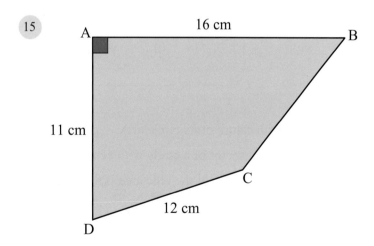

Calculate the area of quadrilateral ABCD if angle BCD = 115°.

Give your answer to one decimal place.

ANSWERS

PART 1

Number 1   Page 1
(ref. Higher GCSE Maths 4–9 Unit 1)

1 £185.83

2 $7\frac{11}{15}$

3 Cresswall Cinema by taxi (£15.40 per person)
(Cresswall by bus £15.50 per person, Albert by taxi £15.60 per person)

4 $3\sqrt{5}, \sqrt{46}, \sqrt{47}, 4\sqrt{3}, 7, 5\sqrt{2}$

5 5 boxes

6 40 litres

7 Katrina correct eg. $\sqrt{4} + \sqrt{9} \neq \sqrt{13}$

8 $n = 3$

9 (a) 57p   (b) 58p

10 $\frac{409}{4995} = \frac{818}{9990}, 0.0\dot{8}1\dot{7} = \frac{817}{9990}$

11 $\frac{11}{15}$

12 Both areas are equal to 2 cm²

13 No, eg. π and $\sqrt{2}$ cannot be written as fractions

14 8p per minute

Number 2   Page 5
(ref. Higher GCSE Maths 4–9 Unit 2)

1 SURE account more by 46p

2 false, eg. $0.1^2 = 0.01 < 0.1$

3 £115.68

4 (a) percentage should not be calculated using the new cost
(b) £60

5 new golf balls are more expensive by £1.50

6 88 chocolate cookies

7 $2^n \div 2^n = 2^{n-n} = 2^0$ and $2^n \div 2^n = 1$ so $2^0 = 1$

8 12

9 1:8

10 30 boxes

11 53.3%

12 £2.43

13 (a) Maybe $27^{-\frac{1}{3}} = -3$ and $4^{-\frac{1}{2}} = -2$
(b) $\frac{8}{3}$

14 1:4

15 30th May

Mixed 1   Page 9
(ref. Higher GCSE Maths 4–9 Units 1, 2)

1 18%

2 $\frac{47}{56}$

3 USA

4 26.7%

5 motorcycle racing cheaper by £2.40

6 No. Company A profit increase is 10.25% not 10%

7 eg. $48a^4b^3 \div 2ab, 240a^5b^6 \div 10a^2b^4, 72a^{10}b^{10} \div 3a^7b^8$

8 20577

9 during the year 2025

10 £23.35 profit

11 $m = 275, n = 11$ and $m = 325, n = 13$

12 skis from shop B, jackets from shop C and ski passes from shop A. Total €839

13 £880.58

14 Techshow (£197.60 Techshow, £198 Marleys, £200.60 E-market)

15 90%

Geometry 1   Page 14
(ref. Higher GCSE Maths 4–9 Unit 3)

1 $A\widehat{C}B = A\widehat{B}C = 59°$ so isosceles

2 130°

3 48°

4 132°

5 $2x$

6 $180 - x$

7 PR̂Q would have to be 90° (angle in a semi-circle) but is actually 91°

8 36°

9 should be 70°

11 200°

12 $90 + x$

13 35°

15 42°

Mixed 2   Page 18

(ref. Higher GCSE Maths 4–9 Units 1, 2, 3)

1 Eva by £69

2 21.4%

3 24

4 12

5 £98.25

6 $x = 24°$, angles are 106° and 74°

7 Two 1.5 litre cartons and one 2 litre carton: total cost £9.50

8 $2^0 \div 2^n = \dfrac{1}{2^n}$ and $2^0 \div 2^n = 2^{0-n} = 2^{-n}$ so $2^{-n} = \dfrac{1}{2^n}$

9 3640

10 £12 433.92

11 Timon is correct $(3\sqrt{2} - 2\sqrt{2} = \sqrt{2})$

12 £438.65

13 $180 - (180 - x) = x$

14 TECHPALACE (£393.60) is the best deal, (TEKNIHAUS £402, COMPUTERDRIVE £397.50)

15 $1\frac{17}{30}$ miles

Algebra 1   Page 22

(ref. Higher GCSE Maths 4–9 Unit 4)

1 $\frac{9}{16}$

3 eg. $x = 3, y = 2, z = 1$

4 (b) $4\,\text{m} \times 6\,\text{m} \times 9\,\text{m}$

5 $60x$

6 $4x + 32$

7 should be $x^2 + 8x + 16 + 12x + 6 = x^2 + 20x + 22$

8 $n = 3$

9 (a) $V = 12x^3 + 34x^2 + 24x$
   (b) $M = 12x^3y + 34x^2y + 24xy$

10 98 cm

11 $12x + 8$

12 (b) $6\,\text{m} \times 4\,\text{m}$

13 $x^2 - 50x + 600 = 0$ hence the numbers are 20 and 30

14 $a = 4, p = 15, q = -2$

15 (b) 24

Mixed 3   Page 26

(ref. Higher GCSE Maths 4–9 Units 1, 2, 3, 4)

1 £7500

2 London. An extra 8.46 euros

3 $y = 540 - 4x$

4 Yes, the cost is £14.10

5 480 g box

6 $T_2 = 0$

7 Bank de Reece better by £11

8 $3x^2 + 8x + 4 = (3x + 2)(x + 2)$ so $(x + 4)$ is not a factor

9 Canary Hotel (£4300) is the cheapest. (Pearl Hotel: £4332 and Oyster Hotel: £4654)

10 eg. $(a - b)^2 = a^2 - 2ab + b^2 \neq a^2 - b^2$

11 $2x - 180$

12 3.78%

13 False. $\dfrac{6}{\sqrt{3}} = 2\sqrt{3}$

14 26.46% loss

15 $16x^2 + 40x + 25$

Number 3   Page 31

(ref. Higher GCSE Maths 4–9 Unit 5)

1 13:50

2 (a) 3200   (b) $2\frac{1}{2}$ hours saved

3 greatest = 44 100, least = 38 400

4 $A = 252, B = 700$

5 4.2 (light) years

6 5 glasses

7 (a) $m = 2, n = -2$ or vice versa   (b) 1×10^{-3}

8 £451 584

9 True

10 0.22%

11 36 120 000 computers

12 Lower bound = 200 cm², Upper bound = 242 cm²

13 £22.52

14 M increases by $\frac{1}{2}$

15 6.24 cm

Mixed 4   Page 34
(ref. Higher GCSE Maths 4–9 Units 1, 2, 3, 4, 5)

1 NINE PLAN (£1 cheaper)

2 $12 \times 50p, 20 \times £1$

3 $y = 380 - 3x$

4 £8295.83

5 $T\hat{U}S = U\hat{Q}R = 65°$
so satisfy corresponding angles hence SU parallel to RQ, ie. trapezium

6 27 kg

7 £47 392.80

8 get both powers of 10 to be the same, etc.

9 56.48% profit

10 $(x + 3)(x + 4)$ so not a square

11 $135 - \frac{3x}{2}$

12 72.8% increase

13 18 smaller boxes (larger box is 33 cm × 7 cm × 12 cm)

15 (b) 3 m

Algebra 2   Page 38
(ref. Higher GCSE Maths 4–9 Unit 6)

1 6500

2 (a) 0.75 m/s²   (b) acceleration

3 turning point on axis of symmetry between $x = 2$ and $x = 3$, ie. $x = 2.5$. Substitute this into the equation to find $y = -0.25$

4 Toni has squared each term separately.
The correct answer is $x = m^2 - 2my + y^2 + 2$

5 $y = \frac{3}{2}x - 6$

6 324 cm²

7 (a) Use table:

x	-3	-2	-1	0	1	2	3
y	30	14	4	0	2	10	26

(b) $(0, 0), (\frac{1}{3}, 0)$ (c) $(\frac{1}{6}, \frac{1}{12})$

8 $\frac{x - 40}{3} + \frac{2x + 40}{5} = 310$ so Grace had 860 dollars

9 (b) 7 m

10 $a = \frac{81}{121}$

11 (a) 4 mins
(b) 3 mins (steeper curve)
(c) find gradient by using the tangent.
The tangent would probably not be perfect.

12 $m = -1$

13 any equation equivalent to $y = \frac{1}{2}x + c$ where c is any number

14 (b) 0.3954   (c) 3 times

15 (b) Use table:

x	0	2	4	6	8	10	12	14	16
y	0	120	224	312	384	440	480	504	512

x	18	20	22	24	26	28	30	32
y	504	480	440	384	312	224	120	0

(c) max. area = 512 m², $x = 16$ m

Mixed 5   Page 42
(ref. Higher GCSE Maths 4–9 Units 1, 2, 3, 4, 5, 6)

1 £8.18

2 $170 - 3x$

3 44 cm

4 (a) Yes   (b) No. LCM = 28 600

5 RUNWELL £499.99 (DAWSONS £504, CYCLESTORE £510)

6 $\frac{3n}{40}$

7 EASY BANK (EASY BANK £408, TRICKIER BANK £407.50, MAYBE BANK £400)

8 8000

9 120°

10 £3976

11 Phil is correct. It should be $9 \div 2 = 4.5$

12 12 cm

13 Yes, gradients are -4 and $\frac{1}{4}$

14 £5905.90

15 $5\sqrt{2} - 5$

Statistics 1   Page 47

(ref. Higher GCSE Maths 4–9 Unit 8)

1 (a) $\frac{42}{300} = \frac{7}{50}$ (b) 70

2 $\frac{7}{11}$

3 410

4 $\frac{3}{7}$

5 $\frac{53}{595}$

6 0.4744

7 (a) (ii) is true

   (b)
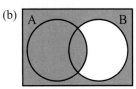

   (c) eg. $(A' \cap B)'$

8 $\frac{15}{272}$

9 $\frac{2}{285}$

10 (a) 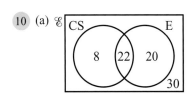   (b) $\frac{11}{40}$ (c) $\frac{11}{21}$

11 (b) 25

12 (a)

H   N

35 (46) 19

(b) (i) $\frac{46}{65}$ (ii) $\frac{35}{54}$

13 0.38

14 $\frac{15}{17}$

15 $\dfrac{2m(n - m)}{n(n - 1)}$

Mixed 6   Page 51

(ref. Higher GCSE Maths 4–9 Units 1, 2, 3, 4, 5, 6, 8)

1 £1385.01

2 280 cm²

3 Sunday (ratio 5:4 will not give whole numbers for 35 animals in total)

4 £3.60

5 Each group of branches covers all possibilities so must add up to 1

6 $180 - 2x$

7 195 cm

8 $x = 1, y = 1; x = 2, y = 4; x = 7, y = 49;$
   $x = 14, y = 196$

10 (a) $a = 4, b = 4$ (b) $(-2, 0)$

11 (a) 10th October full board cheaper by €20.63
    (b) £1722.01

12 $f^{-1}(x)$ should be $\dfrac{x + 3}{5}$ so $x = \dfrac{3}{4}$

13 $\widehat{OCB} = 90 - x$ (angle between tangent and radius is 90°)
    $\widehat{BOC} = 180 - (90 - x) - (90 - x) = 2x$
    (isosceles triangle OBC)
    $\widehat{BAC} = x$ (angle at centre of a circle is twice the angle at the circumference)

15 $M = 6$

Mixed 7   Page 56

(ref. Higher GCSE Maths 4–9 Units 1, 2, 3, 4, 5, 6, 8)

1 15 cm

2 1470

3 Both are correct

4   Belgium

5   (a) $(n^{\frac{1}{3}})^3 = n$ so $n^{\frac{1}{3}} = \sqrt[3]{n}$ (b) $3m^2n^3$

6   $90 - 2x$

7   £23 098.40

8   23

9   (a) £171.02
    (b) household would pay £5.85 more with
        Cotswold Electricity Company

10 85

11 (a) $\dfrac{180}{n}$ (b) $3°$

12 11.875 m/s

13 She will choose 'Sunny Places' (£339.97)
    (Jaga Tours £361.83, Easy Stay £361.84)

14 $\frac{11}{40}$

15 $\sqrt{2}$ cm

PART 2

Mixed 8   Page 61

(ref. Higher GCSE Maths 4–9 Units 1, 2, 3, 4, 5, 6, 8)

1   375 g

2   (a) $S\hat{P}R = P\hat{R}Q = 33°$ (alternate angles),
        $P\hat{R}S = R\hat{P}Q = 33°$ (alternate angles) so
        triangle PRS is isosceles
    (b) rhombus (triangles PQR and PRS are
        congruent)

3   $x = 4.9$

4   £15 683

5   (a) 'identical to', ie. true for all values of the
        variables
    (b) Factorise or show both $\equiv 12x^3 - 6x^2 - 12x + 6$

6   Tristar Building Society earns £2.95 more

7   Carl, cheaper by £45

8   August 12th

9   2

11 130°

12 42

14 $x - 90$

15 total time $= 123$ s so Beth did not succeed

Geometry 2   Page 66

(ref. Higher GCSE Maths 4–9 Units 9, 10)

1   1.1 m

2   stand on triangular face (least area)

3   (2, 2), AD invariant and (5, 5), BC invariant

4   £16.52 per hour

5   No, Pete's reach is 3.3 m above the ground but the
    height of the shed is 3.66 m

6   $\overrightarrow{AB} = \begin{pmatrix} 3 \\ 2 \end{pmatrix}$, $\overrightarrow{BC} = \begin{pmatrix} 4 \\ 3 \end{pmatrix}$ and $\overrightarrow{AC} = \begin{pmatrix} 7 \\ 5 \end{pmatrix}$
    so $\overrightarrow{AB} + \overrightarrow{BC} = \overrightarrow{AC}$

7   31.8 m

8   $32x(8x^2 - 3x - 6)$ or $256x^3 - 96x^2 - 192x$

10 £1428.90

12 $x\sqrt{2}$ $(1.41x)$

13 (a) 58 minutes   (b) 14:20

Mixed 9   Page 71

(ref. Higher GCSE Maths 4–9 Units 1, 2, 3, 4, 6, 8, 9, 10)

1   earliest bus: 1835; arrives home at 1926

2   84 cm²

3   180° rotation about (a, b) and an enlargement
    factor k about (a, b)

4   £18.75 loss

5   340 g tin is the best value

6   $20n^3 + 48n^2 + 32n = 4n(5n^2 + 12n + 8)$

7   (a) slowing down, negative gradient
    (b) acceleration $= -3$ or deceleration $= 3$
    (c) m/s²

8   694 575

9   1800

10 $4\sqrt{5} - 2\sqrt{5} = 2\sqrt{5} = \sqrt{20}$

11 $x = 180 - \dfrac{360}{n}$

12 $\overrightarrow{QT} = \overrightarrow{RS} = 3a + b$ and $\overrightarrow{RQ} = \overrightarrow{ST} = 2a$ so
    QRST is a parallelogram

13 $x = 18.1$ m, $h = 7.3$ m

14 Eve has reversed the order of the functions when
    creating the composite functions.

140

15 angles BAC and PQR are both 90°, AB = QR
(= radius), BC = PR (= 2 × radius) so congruent
(RHS)

Statistics 2   Page 76

(ref. Higher GCSE Maths 4–9 Unit 11)

1 any suitable chart or diagram

2 43

4 20% increase

5 (a) negative correlation
(b) depends on line of best fit
(c) the given data is only in the 1–5 year age
range

6 92

7 (a) Each member has an equal probability of
being chosen
(b) No. Natalia's method should but Anton's
approach is not fair (paper not of equal size,
pieces stick together so not properly mixed
up)

8 Yes, assuming a Winter decline in sales

9 any suitable diagram or chart

10 (a) 8   (b) 73

11 $n < 60°$

12 18

13 250

14 (a) around 10, depending on line of best fit
(b) 1 drink, 30°C max. temp.
(c) outside the data range (would actually get a
negative number of drinks)

15 210

Mixed 10   Page 82

(ref. Higher GCSE Maths 4–9 Units 1, 2, 3, 4, 5, 6, 8,
10, 11)

1 the 500 ml cup

2 any suitable diagram or chart

3 not completely factorised,
should be $4x(x + 3)(x - 3)$

4 7

5 Henton Rovers scored 6 more goals (60 to 54)

6 (b) positive correlation
(c) depends on line of best fit
(d) not reliable, outside the data range, would
give a negative shoe size

7 28.5 mins

8 £413.60

9 12 cm²

10 $p(A' \cup B) = 0.9 > 0.8$ ℰ

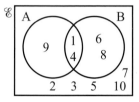

11 $7x - 30 + 3x + 10 = 180$ (opposite angles in a
cyclic quadrilateral add up to 180°) so $x = 20°$
hence angles in PQRS are 110°, 70°, 70°, 110°.
PQRS is therefore a trapezium

12 7.65 m

13 (0, 2)

14 $y = 135 - x$

15 10 g/cm³

Algebra 3   Page 87

(ref. Higher GCSE Maths 4–9 Unit 12)

1 $x = 1.18$

2 (5, 1)

3 yes with $n = 12$

4 razor 90p and shaving brush £2.40

5 $x + \dfrac{b}{2a} = \pm\dfrac{\sqrt{b^2 - 4ac}}{2a} \Rightarrow x = \dfrac{-b}{2a} \pm \dfrac{\sqrt{b^2 - 4ac}}{2a}$

$\Rightarrow x = \dfrac{-b \pm \sqrt{b^2 - 4ac}}{2a}$

6 7.8 seconds

7 60 adults

8 (a) $m = 200$ (b) $n = 2$
(c) 415   (d) 5th year

9 (a) Use table:

x	−3	−2	−1	0	1	2	3
y	33	16	5	0	1	8	21

(b) 0, 0.7   (c) −1.2, 1.9   (d) −0.9, 1.5

10 $m = 8, n = 5$

11 5 units

12 25 square units

13 0.244 g

14 A 50 g, B 20 g

15 3.58 km

Mixed 11 Page 91

(ref. Higher GCSE Maths 4–9 Units 1, 2, 3, 4, 6, 8, 9, 10, 11, 12)

1 Yes, sister gets £78.80

2 triangle ABC: 60°, 70°, 50° and triangle PQR: 40°, 55°, 85°

3 $(-4, 4)$

4 $y = 360 - 2x$

5 35

6 during the 7th year

7 5 hours 39 minutes

8 No, he should have taken x out as a common factor,

$x(2c - a) = y + bd$ hence $x = \dfrac{y + bd}{2c - a}$

9 £58.80

10 $(3\sqrt{3}, 1)$

11 22

12 angle AOC $= 360 - (180 - 2x) - (180 - 2y) = 2(x + y)$
'angle at centre is twice angle at circumference'

13 4 green and 12 white

14 (b) 7.53 m/s

15 $6x^3 + 54x^2$

Geometry 3 Page 95

(ref. Higher GCSE Maths 4–9 Unit 13)

1 Field A more expensive by £26.62

2 90.9%

3 gravel B cheaper by £20

4 9

5 AB:AC $= 11:19$ but AE:AD $= 10:18 = 5:9$ so triangles ABE and ACD are not similar. Angles in the triangles do not correspond so BE is not parallel to CD.

6 Three 2.5 litre tins for a total of £55.50

7 11.9%

8 £20.25

9 16.2 cm²

10 3.97 m

11 $120x^2$

12 £222.28

13 1536π

14 13 080 cm³ or 0.013 m³

15 $64\pi\sqrt{3}$ cm³

Mixed 12 Page 101

(ref. Higher GCSE Maths 4–9 Units 2, 3, 4, 5, 10, 12, 13, 16)

1 (a) $3\frac{1}{3} : \frac{5}{6} = 20:5 = 4:1$ so $\frac{4}{5}$ are yellow (Oscar correct)

(b) $\dfrac{5n}{4}$

2 (a) Melanie earns £16 more
(b) Robert earns £84 more

3 1554 m

4 (a) eg. washing machine width may be 68.5 cm and the gap may be 67.5 cm
(b) 1.15 m² (11 500 cm²)

5 £44.47

6 36.0 cm²

7 20

8 33.4 cm

9 $\sqrt{\text{area ratio}} = \sqrt[3]{\text{volume ratio}}$ so P and Q are similar

10 eg. $(2n + 1)^2 = 4n^2 + 4n + 1 = 2(2n^2 + 2n) + 1$, ie. odd

11 10 176 cm²

12 (a) Use table:

x	-2	-1	0	1	2	3
y	-12	0	2	0	0	8

(b) read off x-values where $y = 0$, ie. -1, 1, 2

(c) 2.7

(d) rearrange into $x^3 - 2x^2 - x + 2 = -2$ then read off x-values where $y = -2$, ie. -1.3

13 $\dfrac{7x(x - 6)}{7x - 30}$

14 £45

15 $5 < x \leqslant 7$

Statistics 3   Page 106

(ref. Higher GCSE Maths 4–9 Unit 14)

1 mean = 3.6, median = 4

2 (a) $\frac{1}{5}$ (b) 20

(c) any suitable statements using Bristol median 22 and range 45 against Birmingham median 23 and range 28

3 6 pairs

4 The Sabres win by 2.3 seconds

5 11

6 Any suitable comparisons, eg. Premiership (Median = 52, range = 56 and Championship median = 67, range = 54, etc.)

7 (a) Gina used mid-values not upper values, 30 plotted in place of 34 for cumulative frequency

(b) IQ description, ie. position $\frac{1}{4}(78/9)$ and position $\frac{3}{4}(78/9)$ then read off marks and subtract for IQ range

8 (a) 7 pupils

(b) Suitable comparisons using spread and medians
(Class 11P: min = 12, LQ = 32, median = 48, UQ = 74, max = 98
Class 11Q: min = 26, LQ = 40, median = 58, UQ = 66, max = 90)

9 $\frac{9}{160}$

10 (a) Use gardener 1 cumulative frequencies: 5, 14, 28, 38, 63, 79, 91, 99, 100 and gardener 2 cumulative frequencies: 8, 18, 33, 50, 80, 110, 116, 120

(b) suitable comparisons (gardener 1: LQ = 116, median = 150, UQ = 174, IQ range = 58 and gardener 2: LQ = 117, median = 148, UQ = 166, IQ range = 49)

11 $\frac{54}{193}$

12 3

13 28

14 (a) Yes. Lower quartile is £21 000

(b) Suitable comparisons using spread and medians.
(Hensons: min = 14, LQ = 21, median = 26, UQ = 28, max = 39)
(Tadweld: min = 19, LQ = 25, median = 31, UQ = 32, max = 38)

15 mean = 1.76

Mixed 13   Page 113

(ref. Higher GCSE Maths 4–9 Units 1, 2, 3, 4, 8, 10, 12, 13, 14, 16)

1 314.2 cm²

2 £1500 (6 m × 8 m and 6 m × 2 m)

3 27 cm

4 p(short or blue) = p(short) + p(blue) − p(blue short) so Henry is not correct because he needs to subtract p(blue short sleeved shirt)

5 2 cm

6 any suitable comparison
(City: mean estimate = 5.9, range = 15)

7 25.0 cm

8 £104.49

9 7.3 km

10 Yes, 859 is the 20th term in the sequence.

11 (a) 13.3%

(b) Suitable comparisons using spread and medians (Harris Furniture Firm: LQ = 31, median = 35, UQ = 38, IQ range = 7 and Mason's Sofa Company: LQ = 29, median = 42, UQ = 45, IQ range = 16)

12 (a) any suitable explanation

(b) $(2n + 1) + (2n + 3) + (2n + 5) + (2n + 7)$ $= 8n + 16 = 8(n + 2)$

13 The Magenta Hotel is cheaper by £7.60

14 (a) $V = 5x^3 + 25x^2 + 30x - \dfrac{5\pi x^3}{4}$

(b) $m = 2x\left(5x^3 + 25x^2 + 30x - \dfrac{5\pi x^3}{4}\right)$

15 3:2

Geometry 4   Page 119
(ref. Higher GCSE Maths 4–9 Units 17, 18)

1   Use eg. corresponding angles, angles on a straight line, angles at a point or equivalent

2   No, the car will stop 0.4 miles short

3   (a) $\widehat{CDE} = \widehat{ABC} = 90°$, $\widehat{ECD} = \widehat{BAC}$ (alternate angles) so all 3 angles are the same hence similar triangles

   (b) $\dfrac{756}{25} = 30\frac{6}{25}\,\text{cm}^2$

4   4.2 miles

5   22 m

6   diagonals of a rhombus bisect each other and cross at right angles

7   302°

8   Yes. The diagonal is 16.91 cm long

9   278 cm²

10   47.5 m

11   Bearing 091.2°, distance 22.7 km

12   7.24 cm

13   minimum value of $\sin t$ is -1 at $t = 270°$.
   $h = 4 + 2\sin 270° = 4 - 2 = 2$ hence co-ordinates (270, 2)

14   £4694.97

15   $y = 5(x + 3)^2$

Mixed 14   Page 124
(ref. Higher GCSE Maths 4–9 Units 1, 2, 3, 6, 10, 12, 13, 14, 16, 18)

1   4 rolls, total cost £74

2   $\frac{1}{2}(x + 45)$

3   Any suitable comparison
   (Forest United: mean = 21.65, range = 5, Castle Rangers: mean = 25.8, range = 14)

4   231.4°

5   1720 m in 540 s (9 minutes)

6   (a) £105.06   (b) £157.54

7   (a) 39.6°   (b) 325.0 cm²

8   (a) $(n + 1)(n + 2) - n(n + 3) = 2$
   (b) eg. $(2n - 1)(2n + 1) - (2n - 3)(2n + 3) = 8$

9   Deal 3 (£378) better than Deal 1 (£390) and Deal 2 (£425)

10   54

11   $2\frac{11}{6}$, ie. $k = \frac{11}{6}$

12   84

13   square pyramid greater by 21.1 cm³

14   10

15   $(-5, 0)$

Mixed 15   Page 130
(ref. Higher GCSE Maths 4–9 Units 1, 2, 4, 6, 8, 10, 12, 13, 14, 18)

1   12

2   £10.20

3   37.5%

4   £51.75

5   27

6   283°

7   $\dfrac{n}{10}\,\text{km/h} = \dfrac{1000n}{10 \times 60 \times 60}\,\text{m/s} = \dfrac{n}{36}\,\text{m/s}$

8   (a) Use cumulative frequencies: 4, 6, 10, 20, 34, 68, 74, 78, 80
   (b) Use: min = 147, LQ = 180, median = 192, UQ = 198, max = 256
   (c) Suitable comparisons using Hanford values from part (b) with Matwick values: min = 174, LQ = 200, median = 226, UQ = 242, max = 268

9   Not correct. Should factorise to $(2x + 1)(3x - 4)$ to give $x = \frac{4}{3}$ cm

10   25.1°

12   $40\pi\,\text{cm}^2$

13   Amber pays £2504 more tax

14   (5, 12)

15   147.9 cm²

Question Index 14(6) means Page 14 Question 6